Connected 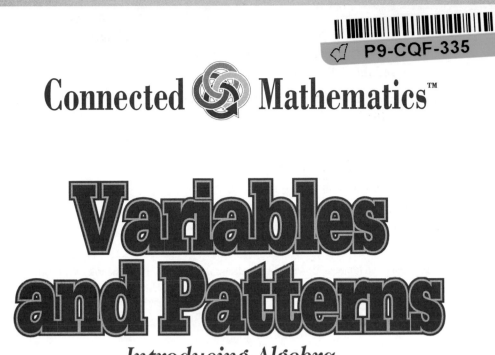 Mathematics™

Variables and Patterns

Introducing Algebra

Teacher's Guide

Glenda Lappan

James T. Fey

William M. Fitzgerald

Susan N. Friel

Elizabeth Difanis Phillips

PEARSON

Prentice
Hall

Needham, Massachusetts

Upper Saddle River, New Jersey

The Connected Mathematics™ Project was developed at Michigan State University with financial support from the Michigan State University Office of the Provost, Computing and Technology, and the College of Natural Science.

This material is based upon work supported by the National Science Foundation under Grant No. MDR 9150217.

This project was supported, in part,
by the
National Science Foundation
Opinions expressed are those of the authors
and not necessarily those of the Foundation

The Michigan State University authors and administration have agreed that all MSU royalties arising from this publication will be devoted to purposes supported by the Department of Mathematics and the MSU Mathematics Education Enrichment Fund.

Photo Acknowledgements: 16 (Chicago) © Jean-Claude Lejeune/Stock, Boston; 16 (Melbourne) © Joe Carini/The Image Works; 18 © Rick Smolan/Stock, Boston; 22 © Fredrik Bodin/Stock, Boston; 23 © William Johnson/Stock, Boston; 24 © Larry Mulvehill/The Image Works; 32 © Duomo Inc.; 36 © Joe McBride/Tony Stone Images; 42 © Addison Geary/Stock, Boston; 51 © E. Strenk, Superstock, Inc.; 57 © Topham/The Image Works

PEARSON
Prentice
Hall

ISBN 0-13-180789-7

3 4 5 6 7 8 9 10   07 06 05 04 03

The Connected Mathematics Project Staff

Project Directors

James T. Fey
University of Maryland

William M. Fitzgerald
Michigan State University

Susan N. Friel
University of North Carolina at Chapel Hill

Glenda Lappan
Michigan State University

Elizabeth Difanis Phillips
Michigan State University

Project Manager

Kathy Burgis
Michigan State University

Technical Coordinator

Judith Martus Miller
Michigan State University

Collaborating Teachers/Writers

Mary K. Bouck
Portland, Michigan

Jacqueline Stewart
Okcmos, Michigan

Curriculum Development Consultants

David Ben-Chaim
Weizmann Institute

Alex Friedlander
Weizmann Institute

Eleanor Geiger
University of Maryland

Jane Mitchell
University of North Carolina at Chapel Hill

Anthony D. Rickard
Alma College

Evaluation Team

Mark Hoover
Michigan State University

Diane V. Lambdin
Indiana University

Sandra K. Wilcox
Michigan State University

Judith S. Zawojcwski
National-Louis University

Graduate Assistants

Scott J. Baldridge
Michigan State University

Angie S. Eshelman
Michigan State University

M. Faaiz Gierdien
Michigan State University

Jane M. Keiser
Indiana University

Angela S. Krebs
Michigan State University

James M. Larson
Michigan State University

Ronald Preston
Indiana University

Tat Ming Sze
Michigan State University

Sarah Theule-Lubienski
Michigan State University

Jeffrey J. Wanko
Michigan State University

Field Test Production Team

Katherine Oesterle
Michigan State University

Stacey L. Otto
University of North Carolina at Chapel Hill

Teacher/Assessment Team

Kathy Booth
Waverly, Michigan

Anita Clark
Marshall, Michigan

Julie Faulkner
Traverse City, Michigan

Theodore Gardella
Bloomfield Hills, Michigan

Yvonne Grant
Portland, Michigan

Linda R. Lobue
Vista, California

Suzanne McGrath
Chula Vista, California

Nancy McIntyre
Troy, Michigan

Mary Beth Schmitt
Traverse City, Michigan

Linda Walker
Tallahassee, Florida

Software Developer

Richard Burgis
East Lansing, Michigan

Development Center Directors

Nicholas Branca
San Diego State University

Dianne Briars
Pittsburgh Public Schools

Frances R. Curcio
New York University

Perry Lanier
Michigan State University

J. Michael Shaughnessy
Portland State University

Charles Vonder Embse
Central Michigan University

Field Test Coordinators

Michelle Bohan
Queens, New York

Melanie Branca
San Diego, California

Alecia Devantier
Shepherd, Michigan

Jenny Jorgensen
Flint, Michigan

Sandra Kralovec
Portland, Oregon

Sonia Marsalis
Flint, Michigan

William Schaeffer
Pittsburgh, Pennsylvania

Karma Vince
Toledo, Ohio

Virginia Wolf
Pittsburgh, Pennsylvania

Shirel Yaloz
Queens, New York

Student Assistants

Laura Hammond
David Roche
Courtney Stoner
Jovan Trpovski
Julie Valicenti
Michigan State University

Patricia Wagner
Holmes Middle School

Greg Williams
Gundry Elementary School

Lansing

Susan Bissonette
Waverly Middle School

Kathy Booth
Waverly East Intermediate School

Carole Campbell
Waverly East Intermediate School

Gary Gillespie
Waverly East Intermediate School

Denise Kehren
Waverly Middle School

Virginia Larson
Waverly East Intermediate School

Kelly Martin
Waverly Middle School

Laurie Metevier
Waverly East Intermediate School

Craig Paksi
Waverly East Intermediate School

Tony Pecoraro
Waverly Middle School

Helene Rewa
Waverly East Intermediate School

Arnold Stiefel
Waverly Middle School

Portland

Bill Carlton
Portland Middle School

Kathy Dole
Portland Middle School

Debby Flate
Portland Middle School

Yvonne Grant
Portland Middle School

Terry Keusch
Portland Middle School

John Manzini
Portland Middle School

Mary Parker
Portland Middle School

Scott Sandborn
Portland Middle School

Shepherd

Steve Brant
Shepherd Middle School

Marty Brock
Shepherd Middle School

Cathy Church
Shepherd Middle School

Ginny Crandall
Shepherd Middle School

Craig Ericksen
Shepherd Middle School

Natalie Hackney
Shepherd Middle School

Bill Hamilton
Shepherd Middle School

Julie Salisbury
Shepherd Middle School

Sturgis

Sandra Allen
Eastwood Elementary School

Margaret Baker
Eastwood Elementary School

Steven Baker
Eastwood Elementary School

Keith Barnes
Sturgis Middle School

Wilodean Beckwith
Eastwood Elementary School

Darcy Bird
Eastwood Elementary School

Bill Dickey
Sturgis Middle School

Ellen Eisele
Sturgis Middle School

James Hoelscher
Sturgis Middle School

Richard Nolan
Sturgis Middle School

J. Hunter Raiford
Sturgis Middle School

Cindy Sprowl
Eastwood Elementary School

Leslie Stewart
Eastwood Elementary School

Connie Sutton
Eastwood Elementary School

Traverse City

Maureen Bauer
Interlochen Elementary School

Ivanka Berskshire
East Junior High School

Sarah Boehm
Courtade Elementary School

Marilyn Conklin
Interlochen Elementary School

Nancy Crandall
Blair Elementary School

Fran Cullen
Courtade Elementary School

Eric Dreier
Old Mission Elementary School

Lisa Dzierwa
Cherry Knoll Elementary School

Ray Fouch
West Junior High School

Ed Hargis
Willow Hill Elementary School

Richard Henry
West Junior High School

Dessie Hughes
Cherry Knoll Elementary School

Ruthanne Kladder
Oak Park Elementary School

Bonnie Knapp
West Junior High School

Sue Laisure
Sabin Elementary School

Stan Malaski
Oak Park Elementary School

Jody Meyers
Sabin Elementary School

Marsha Myles
East Junior High School

Mary Beth O'Neil
Traverse Heights Elementary School

Jan Palkowski
East Junior High School

Karen Richardson
Old Mission Elementary School

Kristin Sak
Bertha Vos Elementary School

Mary Beth Schmitt
East Junior High School

Mike Schrotenboer
Norris Elementary School

Gail Smith
Willow Hill Elementary School

Karrie Tufts
Eastern Elementary School

Mike Wilson
East Junior High School

Tom Wilson
West Junior High School

Minnesota

Minneapolis

Betsy Ford
Northeast Middle School

New York

East Elmhurst

Allison Clark
Louis Armstrong Middle School

Dorothy Hershey
Louis Armstrong Middle School

J. Lewis McNeece
Louis Armstrong Middle School

Rossana Perez
Louis Armstrong Middle School

Merna Porter
Louis Armstrong Middle School

Marie Turini
Louis Armstrong Middle School

North Carolina

Durham

Everly Broadway
Durham Public Schools

Thomas Carson
Duke School for Children

Mary Hebrank
Duke School for Children

Bill O'Connor
Duke School for Children

Ruth Pershing
Duke School for Children

Peter Reichert
Duke School for Children

Elizabeth City

Rita Banks
Elizabeth City Middle School

Beth Chaundry
Elizabeth City Middle School

Amy Cuthbertson
Elizabeth City Middle School

Deni Dennison
Elizabeth City Middle School

Jean Gray
Elizabeth City Middle School

John McMenamin
Elizabeth City Middle School

Nicollette Nixon
Elizabeth City Middle School

Malinda Norfleet
Elizabeth City Middle School

Joyce O'Neal
Elizabeth City Middle School

Clevie Sawyer
Elizabeth City Middle School

Juanita Shannon
Elizabeth City Middle School

Terry Thorne
Elizabeth City Middle School

Rebecca Wardour
Elizabeth City Middle School

Leora Winslow
Elizabeth City Middle School

Franklinton

Susan Haywood
Franklinton Elementary School

Clyde Melton
Franklinton Elementary School

Louisburg

Lisa Anderson
Terrell Lane Middle School

Jackie Frazier
Terrell Lane Middle School

Pam Harris
Terrell Lane Middle School

Ohio

Toledo

Bonnie Bias
Hawkins Elementary School

Marsha Jackish
Hawkins Elementary School

Lee Jagodzinski
DeVeaux Junior High School

Norma J. King
Old Orchard Elementary School

Margaret McCready
Old Orchard Elementary School

Carmella Morton
DeVeaux Junior High School

Karen C. Rohrs
Hawkins Elementary School

Marie Sahloff
DeVeaux Junior High School

L. Michael Vince
McTigue Junior High School

Brenda D. Watkins
Old Orchard Elementary School

Oregon

Canby

Sandra Kralovec
Ackerman Middle School

Portland

Roberta Cohen
Catlin Gabel School

David Ellenberg
Catlin Gabel School

Sara Normington
Catlin Gabel School

Karen Scholte-Arce
Catlin Gabel School

West Linn

Marge Burack
Wood Middle School

Tracy Wygant
Athey Creek Middle School

Pennsylvania

Pittsburgh

Sheryl Adams
Reizenstein Middle School

Sue Barie
Frick International Studies Academy

Suzie Berry
Frick International Studies Academy

Richard Delgrosso
Frick International Studies Academy

Janet Falkowski
Frick International Studies Academy

Joanne George
Reizenstein Middle School

Harriet Hopper
Reizenstein Middle School

Chuck Jessen
Reizenstein Middle School

Ken Labuskes
Reizenstein Middle School

Barbara Lewis
Reizenstein Middle School

Sharon Mihalich
Reizenstein Middle School

Marianne O'Connor
Frick International Studies Academy

Mark Sammartino
Reizenstein Middle School

Washington

Seattle

Chris Johnson
University Preparatory Academy

Rick Purn
University Preparatory Academy

Contents

Unit Introduction

Overview	1a
The Mathematics in *Variables and Patterns*	1b
Mathematical and Problem-Solving Goals	1f
Summary of Investigations	1g
Materials	1h
Technology	1h
Resources	1i
Pacing Chart	1i
Variables and Patterns Vocabulary	1j
Assessment Summary	1k
Connections to Other Units	1l

Introducing Your Students to *Variables and Patterns*	2
Mathematical Highlights	4
Using This Teacher's Edition	4a
Investigation 1: Variables and Coordinate Graphs	4b
Student Pages	5
Teaching the Investigation	17a
Investigation 2: Graphing Change	17f
Student Pages	18
Teaching the Investigation	35a
Investigation 3: Analyzing Graphs and Tables	35l
Student Pages	36
Teaching the Investigation	48a
Investigation 4: Patterns and Rules	48n
Student Pages	49
Teaching the Investigation	60a
Investigation 5: Using a Graphing Calculator	60j
Student Pages	61
Teaching the Investigation	68a
Looking Back and Looking Ahead: Unit Reflections	68f
Assessment Resources	69
Blackline Masters	99
Additional Practice	131
Descriptive Glossary	148
Spanish Glossary	150
Index	151

Situations that change are a part of everyone's life. Some situations change in a predictable pattern. Others change in ways that seem beyond our ability to anticipate. It is human nature to want to analyze, anticipate, and predict why things change. Learning to observe, describe, and record changes is the first step in analyzing and searching for patterns in a real-world situation.

Variables and Patterns, the first unit of the Connected Mathematics™ algebra strand, develops students' ability to explore a variety of situations in which changes occur. The setting within which these situations occur is the formation of a company that arranges bicycle tours.

In the first part of the unit, students explore three ways of representing a changing situation. The first way is to describe an event narratively. The second is to use a data table that documents the changes in two variables. The third is to make a graph showing the changes in two variables. These three methods of organizing and recording data are revisited throughout the first part of the unit. They are compared to one another to elicit the strengths of each presentation.

In the rest of the unit, students search for and verbalize patterns of change that relate one variable to another. The introduction of a symbolic expression as a shorter, quicker way to give a written summary of the relationship between two variables comes only after extensive time and effort is devoted to analyzing data sets showing change and describing the changes in words. The advantages of a symbolic rule over a data table or graph are investigated. After becoming proficient in writing symbolic rules, students will learn how to use graphing calculators to make tables and graphs for any given rule.

The relationship between two variables—in particular, the way in which one variable changes in relation to another—is an important idea in mathematics. It is central to understanding functions and concepts in calculus. This unit develops methods for representing these relationships and patterns of change. Verbal descriptions, tables, and graphs are the central representations in this unit. Toward the end of the unit, written and symbolic rules are introduced. This unit provides the basis from which to study other algebra units, such as *Say It with Symbols,* in which the focus is on symbolic reasoning, or *Moving Straight Ahead,* in which the focus is on linear relationships—that is, as one variable changes, the other variable changes by a constant amount.

Each representation has its advantages and disadvantages in promoting understanding of relationships and patterns of change.

Verbal Descriptions

Verbal descriptions of a relationship are useful because they are descriptions in students' everyday language. This helps the students form mental pictures of the situations and the relationships among the variables. The disadvantages of verbal descriptions are that they are sometimes ambiguous, making it difficult to get a quick overview of the situation and the relationships among variables in the situation.

Tables

Tables are easy to read. From a table, it is easy to see how a unit change in one variable affects the change in the other variable. Students can recognize whether the change is additive, multiplicative, or unpredictable. Once students recognize the pattern of change, they can apply it to the variables to get the next entry. For example, consider the following two tables.

Table 1: Linear Relation

x	y
$^-1$	0
0	3
1	6
2	9

Table 2: Exponential Relation

x	y
0	1
1	2
2	4
3	8

In Table 1, as the variable x changes by one unit, the variable y changes by 3 units. The table could be continued by adding 1 to the previous entry in the x column and 3 to the previous entry in the y column. If x is 3, then y is $9 + 3$, or 12. The table can be generated backwards by reversing the pattern of change. If x is $^-2$, then y is 0 minus 3, or $^-3$. The particular change pattern in Table 1 is indicative of all *linear relations.* It is an additive pattern because the rate of change between the two variables is always constant.

The change pattern in Table 2 is characteristic of an *exponential relation.* It is a multiplicative pattern because the variable y is doubling or is increasing by a factor of 2 as the variable x increases by one unit.

In some tables, the patterns of change are not regular. For example, Table 3, which occurs in the second investigation, does not show a pattern of change that is regular; that is, there is no way to predict the change from one point to the next.

Table 3

Time (hours)	Distance (miles)
0	0
0.5	8
1.0	15
1.5	19
2.0	25
2.5	27
3.0	34
3.5	40
4.0	40
4.5	40
5.0	45

Graphs

Graphs are another way to view the relationship and the patterns of change between the variables, such as in Tables 1 and 2. Graphs 1 and 2 can be thought of as pictures of the relationships shown in those tables.

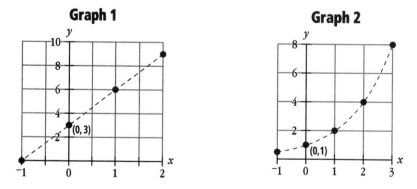

The linearity or constant rate of change is represented by a straight-line graph, while the exponential relation or multiplicative rate of change is characterized by a curved line. These relationships can be represented symbolically as $y = 3x + 3$ (Table 1 and Graph 1) and $y = 2^x$ (Table 2 and Graph 2). Both of these patterns are explored in future units. Linear relationships are the focus of *Moving Straight Ahead*, and exponential growth is studied in *Growing, Growing, Growing*.

This unit provides a firm foundation to continue to study important patterns of change. Only simple linear expressions are explored in this unit. For example, the distance, d, a cyclist can cover depends on time, t, and the rate, r, at which the cyclist peddles. If a cyclist rides at 10 miles per hour, then $d = 10t$. This is a linear relation—its graph is a straight line.

Connecting Points

Many situations are discrete relationships, such as the number of sweatshirts sold and the revenue. If the shirts sell for $5.50, then the revenue, r, for selling n shirts is $r = 5.50n$. In this situation, it does not make sense to connect the points. Points $(1, 5.50)$ and $(2, 11)$ are on the graph; however, if these two points are connected it would imply that $1\frac{1}{2}$ or part of a shirt could be sold. Other situations, such as the distance/time/rate relation, are not discrete; they are continuous. For example, if a bicyclist peddles at a rate of 10 miles per hour, then distance, d, after t hours is $d = 10t$. In the graph of $d = 10t$, it is reasonable to connect the points $(1, 10)$ and $(4, 40)$ since one can travel $1\frac{1}{2}$ hours and go a distance of 15 miles; it makes sense because time is a continuous quantity.

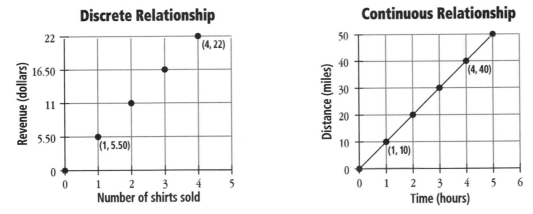

In a distance/time/rate situation, students are asked to decide whether the points can be connected and if so, how they can be connected. For example, the points representing the time and distance of a cyclist can be connected in many ways. A straight line connecting the starting and ending points for a day's ride implies that the cyclist traveled at a constant rate. The four graphs below show other ways these two points may be connected.

- Graph I represents a person who started fast, tired, and rode slowly to the destination.
- Graph II represents a person who rode slowly at first and gradually increased speed.
- Graph III represents a person who started late and rode quickly.
- Graph IV represents a person who rode quickly and reached the destination early.

Selecting a Scale

Another aspect of graphing is that of scale. This is closely connected to the range of values for each variable. To represent a relation graphically, students must have a good feel for the range of values. Students must select an appropriate scale so that the relevant pieces of the graph can be displayed. The effects of the scale can often lead to distortion as shown in the graphs below. For example, suppose students select a scale of 1 to 10 for both axes when they graph the equation $d = 10t$, as in Graph A. Only the information about the first hour would be shown on this graph. This may not be enough information for students to understand the relationship. The scale in Graph B may lead students to believe that the distance covered in three hours is minimal. Graph C more nearly mirrors the situation.

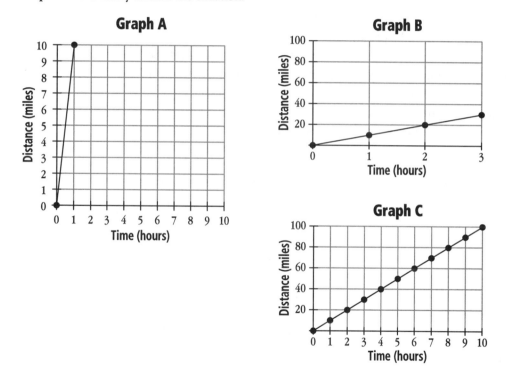

While the relationship between the variables is the most important idea in this unit, it is the representation of these relationships that is the dominant theme. It is important for students to move freely among the various representations. It may not be obvious initially to students how the entries in a table relate to points on a graph or to solutions of a symbolic statement; and conversely, how solutions to an equation or a graph relate to the other representations; however, these connections are explored in depth in this unit.

By the end of the unit, students should feel very comfortable with tables and graphs and with some simple symbolic rules. Students should also have an appreciation of the advantages and disadvantages of each representation. The value of a symbolic rule is that it is brief and represents a complete picture of the pattern, while tables and graphs can represent only parts of the relationships.

Mathematical and Problem-Solving Goals

Variables and Patterns **was created to help students**

- Understand that variables in a situation are those quantities that change, such as time, temperature, feelings, a TV show's popularity, distance traveled, and speed

- Understand that patterns describe a regular or predictable change in data

- Search for patterns of change that show relationships among the variables

- Select an appropriate range of values for the variables

- Create tables, graphs, and simple symbolic rules that describe the patterns of change

- Understand the relationships among forms of representation—words, tables, graphs, and symbolic rules

- Make decisions using tables, graphs, and rules

- Use a graphing calculator for making tables and graphs to find information about a situation

The overall goal of the Connected Mathematics curriculum is to help students develop sound mathematical habits. Through their work in this and other algebra units, students learn important questions to ask themselves about any situation that can be represented and modeled mathematically, such as: *How can mathematics be used to show how quantities change over time? What does it mean when we see regular and predictable changes in a table of data or a graph? How can we use these predictable changes to find out about other possible data? Where in the world around us can we find these patterns? Why do some straight-line graphs rise as x increases, while others fall? When can an equation describe the information in a table? In a graph? When is a graphing calculator helpful in analyzing data? Other than a graph, what information can be found with a graphing calculator?*

Investigation 1: Variables and Coordinate Graphs

Students conduct a jumping jack experiment to explore what happens to a person's ability to perform (endurance) after exerting energy over a period of time. As they graph their jumping jack data, students learn about variables, coordinate axes, choosing appropriate scales for graphs, and plotting data points. They then begin to make interpretations from their graphs.

Investigation 2: Graphing Change

Students look at data collected over a five-day trial run of a bike tour. They learn to examine data and create summary reports, tables, and graphs that show the relationship between distance and time (or speed and time for the fifth day). Students learn more about interpreting tables and graphs, including identifying and explaining changes in intervals and describing any interesting points, such as maximum and minimum points. They also examine what it means to connect a graph's data points in various ways, such as with straight-line segments and curved-line segments, as well as the appropriate situations in which they would connect the points. The advantages and disadvantages of using verbal descriptions, tables, or graphs to represent a situation are explored. Students understand the relationships among these representations and move freely among them.

Investigation 3: Analyzing Graphs and Tables

Students consider business questions involved with running bicycle tours. They learn to make and interpret graphs and tables for a variety of situations involving number of customers, costs, income, and profit. Students analyze and compare information presented in tables and graphs to make good business decisions. The patterns of change are more regular and students are encouraged to describe these patterns in words. This is a precursor to the next investigation, in which students use symbolic rules to describe the patterns.

Investigation 4: Patterns and Rules

Students create and analyze tables and graphs of situations involving distance, rate, and time to find a pattern that relates distance and time for a given rate. They are then asked to express this pattern as a rule, first in words and then in symbols. Students also compare the graphs, tables, and symbolic rules for situations of the form $d = rt$ for various rates. Students develop a deeper understanding of the relationships among the various representations, including symbols, and use them all with ease.

Investigation 5: Using a Graphing Calculator

Students use graphing calculators to make tables (if their graphing calculator has this function) and graphs. They begin by exploring the shapes of graphs, then describing the similarities and differences of rules. This is the first exposure to graphing calculators in this curriculum.

Materials

For students

- Labsheet 5.1
- Clock or watch with second hand
- Grid paper (provided as a blackline master and used by students on a daily basis)
- Transparent grids (optional; copy the blackline master onto transparency film)
- Graphing calculators (with the capacity to display a function as a table)
- Paper cutouts of hexagons (optional)
- Colored pencils (optional)

For the teacher

- Transparencies and transparency markers (optional)
- Transparent grid (optional; copy the blackline master onto transparency film)
- Graphing calculator linking cable and software, such as Texas Instruments TI-Graph Link™ (optional)
- Graphing calculator for the overhead (optional)

Technology

Connected Mathematics™ was developed with the belief that calculators should always be available and that students should decide when to use them. In the first four investigations, the calculations involve only simple arithmetic, so nonscientific calculators are adequate.

The graphing calculator is introduced in Investigation 5. This tool allows students to look at many examples quickly and helps them observe patterns and make conjectures about functions. In the teaching notes, examples using the Texas Instruments TI-80 and TI-82 show teachers how to help students use the graphing calculators. If other types of graphing calculators are used, see your reference manual for instructions.

Bringing graphing calculators into the classroom will create some management issues. If you have several classes using the same calculators, you will need to develop a systematic way to deal with issues such as calculator damage and missing calculators. In general, students are happy to have access to the graphing calculators and do not want to lose that privilege; therefore, most teachers have fewer problems with loss or destruction of graphing calculators than with loss or destruction of textbooks and other supplies.

Management ideas that have worked well for other teachers include these tips.

- Send a note to parents at the beginning of the unit. Tell them that graphing calculators are being used in the mathematics class and explain that their teenagers are responsible for the care of these tools when using them. Have parents sign the note accepting responsibility for damaged or missing calculators. Do not allow students to use the calculators until the note is returned to you.

- Engrave all calculators with the school name and an individual number. You may be able to borrow an engraving tool from the local police department.
- Assign a numbered calculator to each student. Each day the student must use the calculator with his or her designated number. If there is damage, the student must report it to the teacher at the beginning of the hour.
- Have students clear the memory of their calculators at the end of each class period.
- Establish a rule that no students may leave the room at the end of the period until all calculators are checked, counted, and stored.
- Develop a storage system so that you can tell at a glance whether all calculators are in place at the end of the period.

Resources

For teachers

Phillips, E., et al., *Patterns and Functions*, NCTM Addenda Grades 5–8 series, Reston, Va.: National Council of Teachers of Mathematics, 1990.

Dugdale, S., and Kibbey, D. *Interpreting Graphs*. Pleasantville, N.Y.: Sunburst 1993.

Pacing Chart

This pacing chart gives estimates of the class time required for each investigation and assessment piece. Shaded rows indicate opportunities for assessment.

Investigations and Assessments	Class Time
1 Variables and Coordinate Graphs	3 days
2 Graphing Change	5 days
Check-Up	$\frac{1}{2}$ day
3 Analyzing Graphs and Tables	4 days
4 Patterns and Rules	3 days
Quiz	1 day
5 Using a Graphing Calculator	3 days
Self-Assessment	1 day
Unit Test	1 day

Variables and Patterns Vocabulary

The following words and concepts are used in *Variables and Patterns*. Concepts in the left column are those essential for student understanding of this and future units. The Descriptive Glossary gives descriptions of many of these words.

Essential terms developed in this unit	Terms developed in previous units	Nonessential terms
change	area	dependent variable
coordinate graph	circumference	formula
coordinate pair	diameter	independent variable
distance/time/rate of speed	line plot	range of values
income/cost/profit	mean	
pattern	median	
relationship	mode	
rule	perimeter	
scale	polygon	
table	radius	
variable	symbolic form	
x-axis		
y-axis		
x-coordinate		
y-coordinate		

Assessment Summary

Embedded Assessment

Opportunities for informal assessment of student progress are embedded throughout *Variables and Patterns* in the problems, ACE questions, and Mathematical Reflections. Suggestions for observing as students discover and explore mathematical ideas, for probing to guide their progress in developing concepts and skills, and for questioning to determine their level of understanding can be found in the *Launch, Explore,* or *Summarize* sections of all investigation problems. Some examples:

- Investigation 5, Problem 5.1 *Launch* (page 68a) suggests questions you might ask to help students make conjectures about $y = x$ and $y = x + 3$.

- Investigation 3, Problem 3.2 *Explore* (page 48c) suggests ways to assess your students' understanding of how to choose reasonable labels for the x-axis and the y-axis.

- Investigation 4, Problem 4.2 *Summarize* (page 60d) suggests how you may wish to use dialogue when introducing variables.

ACE Assignments

An ACE (Applications–Connections–Extensions) section appears at the end of each investigation. To help you assign ACE questions, a list of assignment choices is given in the margin next to the reduced student page for each problem. Each list indicates the ACE questions that students should be able to answer after they complete the problem.

Partner Quiz

One quiz, which may be given after Investigation 4, is provided with *Variables and Patterns*. This quiz is designed to be completed by pairs of students with the opportunity for revision based on teacher feedback. You will find the quiz and its answer key in the Assessment Resources section. As an alternative to the quiz provided, you can construct your own quizzes by combining questions from the Question Bank, the quiz, and unassigned ACE problems.

Check-Up

One check-up, which may be given after Investigation 2, is provided for use as a quick quiz or as a warm-up activity. The check-up is designed for students to complete individually. You will find the check-up and its answer key in the Assessment Resources section.

Question Bank

A Question Bank provides additional questions you can use for homework, reviews, or quizzes. You will find the Question Bank and its answer key in the Assessment Resources section.

Notebook/Journal

Students should have notebooks to record and organize their work. In the notebooks will be their journals along with sections for vocabulary, homework, and quizzes and check-ups. In their journals, students can take notes, solve investigation problems, and record their mathematical reflections. You should assess student journals for completeness rather than correctness; journals should be seen as "safe" places where students can try out their thinking. A Notebook Checklist and a Self-Assessment are provided in the Assessment Resources section. The Notebook Checklist helps students organize their notebooks. The Self-Assessment guides students as they review their notebooks to determine which ideas they have mastered and which ideas they still need to work on.

Unit Test

The final assessment for *Variables and Patterns* is a test, an individual assessment piece. You will find the test and its answer key in the Assessment Resources section. Since test items cover concepts taught in the unit, students solve problems similar to those previously done in the student edition. You may wish to talk with students individually concerning their performances on the test. Additional problems can be selected from the Question Bank in the Assessment Resources section if necessary to reteach and retest certain concepts.

The ideas in *Variables and Patterns* build on and connect to several big ideas in other Connected Mathematics units.

Big Idea	Prior Work	Future Work
collecting, organizing, and representing data	gathering data by conducting trials of an experiment or game; organizing data in tables and graphs in order to look for patterns and relationships (*Data About Us*; *How Likely Is It?*)	analyzing patterns to develop concepts of surface area and volume (*Filling and Wrapping*); studying data to develop the concept of linear, exponential, and quadratic functions (*Moving Straight Ahead*; *Growing, Growing, Growing*; *Frogs, Fleas, and Painted Cubes*); gathering and analyzing data about populations (*Samples and Populations*)
identifying patterns and extreme values in data organized in graphs or tables; making inferences about situations based on such information	identifying patterns in number and geometry (*Prime Time*; *Shapes and Designs*); analyzing maximum and minimum values in measurement (*Covering and Surrounding*)	understanding relationships between edge lengths and surface area and volume of three-dimensional figures (*Filling and Wrapping*); identifying maximum and minimum values for a mathematical model or equation (*Thinking with Mathematical Models*; *Frogs, Fleas, and Painted Cubes*)
analyzing a pattern or relationship in a graph or table to identify variables and interpret the relationship between the variables	organizing, displaying, and interpreting data in one- and two-dimensional graphs and tables (*Data About Us*); constructing graphs of the relationship between the dimensions and area of a rectangle when the perimeter is held constant and between the dimensions and perimeter when the area is held constant (*Covering and Surrounding*)	extending tables and graphs to include negative coordinates and quantities (*Accentuate the Negative*); formalizing understandings of linear equations in $y = mx + b$ form (*Moving Straight Ahead*); studying and developing mathematical models (*Thinking with Mathematical Models*); identifying and studying nonlinear patterns of growth (*Growing, Growing, Growing*; *Frogs, Fleas, and Painted Cubes*)
analyzing linear relationships and expressing them as written and symbolic rules	developing operation algorithms for fractions, decimals, and percents (*Bits and Pieces II*); programming a computer in Logo to construct two-dimensional geometric shapes (*Shapes and Designs*)	expressing linear relationships in $y = mx + b$ form (*Moving Straight Ahead*); describing situations with linear models or equations (*Thinking with Mathematical Models*); developing strategies for expressing linear relationships in symbols and for solving linear equations (*Say It with Symbols*)
using graphing calculators to organize and represent data and to analyze linear relationships	producing geometric figures with Logo (*Shapes and Designs*)	using graphing calculators to graph and compare lines (*Moving Straight Ahead*); using graphing calculators to develop and study mathematical models (*Thinking with Mathematical Models*); performing isometries in two dimensions (*Kaleidoscopes, Hubcaps, and Mirrors*)

Introducing Your Students to *Variables and Patterns*

Introduce *Variables and Patterns* to your students by telling them this unit is about the way things change. Read through the three opening questions and the first paragraph with your students. Have students individually work on the first question (list three things about yourself and the world that change). After a few minutes, have students share their ideas with someone near them. Having some pairs share their findings helps all students to think about things that change. You may want to create a list of examples of things that change. Ask questions that require your students to think about how their examples change over time and why these changes happen. Read through the paragraph on variables with your students. Tell your students that, in *Variables and Patterns,* they will explore the idea of variables and how two variables change relative to each other. In this unit, they will perform experiments to gather data and represent that data in tables and in graphs.

Variables and Patterns

When Ben started to play the electric guitar, his skill increased quite rapidly. But over time, as he continued to practice, he seemed to improve more slowly. Sketch a graph to show how Ben's guitar-playing skill progressed over time from when he first started playing. What variables might affect the rate at which his playing improved?

List three things about yourself and the world that change. Explain how some of these changes might be related to each other. For example, your height changes as your age changes. How would you represent these changes in a table or graph?

Compare the rental fees of two companies. East Coast Trucks charges $4.25 for each mile a truck is driven. Philadelphia Truck Rental charges $200 for a week, or any part of a week, and an additional $2.00 for each mile a truck is driven. Which of these two companies offers a better rate? If you were renting a truck, what variables might influence your decision?

All around you, things are changing. Temperatures and tides rise and fall, seasons and moon phases change, prices and the popularity of television shows vary. You are changing too. Your height, weight, hair length, and your moods and tastes are changing. Sometimes there is a relationship in the way two things are changing. For example, the number of hours of daylight changes as the seasons change, and the prices of goods change as consumer demand changes.

In mathematics, quantities that change are called *variables*. In this unit, you will explore variables and the relationships between them. You can show these relationships using things like tables, graphs, and equations. These tools are at the heart of the branch of mathematics called *algebra*.

As you work through the investigations in this unit, you will encounter problems like those on the opposite page.

Explain that there are many important and interesting questions that involve the idea of variables. Again, refer students to the three questions posed on the opening page of the student edition. You may wish to have a class discussion about these questions, but do not worry about finding the "correct" answers at this time. Ask your students to keep these questions in mind as they work through the investigations and to think about how they might use the ideas they are learning to help them determine the answers. Each question is posed again in the investigations, at the time when students have learned the mathematical concepts required to answer it.

Mathematical Highlights

The Mathematical Highlights page was designed to provide information to students and to parents and other family members. This page gives students a preview of the activities and problems in *Variables and Patterns*. As they work through the unit, students can refer back to the Mathematical Highlights page to review what they have learned and to preview what is still to come. This page also tells students' families what mathematical ideas and activities will be covered as the class works through *Variables and Patterns*.

Mathematical Highlights

In *Variables and Patterns* you will explore some of the basic ideas of algebra. The unit should help you to

- Recognize problem situations in which two or more quantitative variables are related to each other;

- Find patterns that help in predicting the values of a dependent variable as values of other related independent variables change;

- Construct tables, graphs, and simple symbolic expressions that describe patterns of change in variables;

- Solve problems and make decisions about variables using information given in tables, graphs, and symbolic expressions; and

- Use a graphing calculator to make tables and graphs of relations between variables and to answer questions about those relations.

As you work on the problems of this unit, ask questions about problem situations that involve related quantities: *What are the variables in the problem? How are the variables in this problem related to each other? What patterns appear in the tables or graphs of relationships among variables? How can those patterns be used to make predictions and answer questions about the related variables?*

The Investigations

The teaching materials for each investigation consist of three parts: an overview, the student pages with teaching outlines, and the detailed notes for teaching the investigation.

The overview of each investigation includes brief descriptions of the problems, the mathematical and problem-solving goals of the investigation, and a list of necessary materials.

Essential information for teaching the investigation is provided in the margins around the student pages. The "At a Glance" overviews are brief outlines of the Launch, Explore, and Summarize phases of each problem for reference as you work with the class. To help you assign homework, a list of "Assignment Choices" is provided next to each problem. Wherever space permits, answers to problems, follow-ups, ACE questions, and Mathematical Reflections appear next to the appropriate student pages.

The Teaching the Investigation section follows the student pages and is the heart of the Connected Mathematics curriculum. This section describes in detail the Launch, Explore, and Summarize phases for each problem. It includes all the information needed for teaching, along with suggestions for guiding the discussion. Use this section to prepare lessons and as needed while teaching an investigation.

Assessment Resources

The Assessment Resources section contains blackline masters and answer keys for the quiz, the check-up, the Unit Test, and the Question Bank. It also provides guidelines for assessing other important student work. Samples of student work, along with the teacher's comments about how each sample was assessed, will help you to evaluate your students' efforts. Blackline masters for the Notebook Checklist and the Self-Assessment support student self-evaluation, an important aspect of assessment in the Connected Mathematics curriculum.

Blackline Masters

The Blackline Masters section includes masters for the labsheet and transparencies. A blackline master of grid paper is also provided.

Additional Practice

Practice pages for each investigation offer additional problems for students who need more practice with the basic concepts developed in the investigations as well as some continual review of earlier concepts.

Descriptive Glossary

The Descriptive Glossary provides descriptions and examples of the key concepts in *Variables and Patterns*. These descriptions are not intended to be formal definitions, but are meant to give you an idea of how students might make sense of these important concepts.

Variables and Coordinate Graphs

The setting for the first investigation is a stamina test involving jumping jacks to help students see what happens when people try to exert energy for a long period of time.

In Problem 1.1, Preparing for a Bicycle Tour, students collect data by performing a simple experiment involving jumping jacks. As they do jumping jacks, they collect data on the total number of jumping jacks they complete in 10-second intervals for 2 minutes. In Problem 1.2, Making Graphs, students use the data they gathered for Problem 1.1 to make a graph. As they make the graph, they are introduced to variables and coordinate axes. In the follow-up questions, they compare the usefulness of graphs and tables for various situations. The ACE questions give students more opportunities to make and interpret tables and graphs and to extend their understanding of variables and how to make a reasonable scale for their graphs.

Mathematical and Problem-Solving Goals

- *To collect data from an experiment and then make a table and a graph to organize and represent the data*

- *To search for explanations for patterns and variations in data*

- *To understand that a variable is a quantity that changes and to recognize variables in the real world*

- *To understand that in order to make a graph that shows the relationship between two variables, you need to identify the two variables, choose an axis for each, and select an appropriate scale for each axis*

- *To interpret information given in a graph*

Materials		
Problem	**For students**	**For the teacher**
All	Graphing calculators	Transparencies 1.1 to 1.2B (optional)
1.1	Clock or watch with second hand	
1.2	Grid paper (provided as a blackline master), transparent grids (optional)	Transparent grid (optional)
ACE	Grid paper	

INVESTIGATION 1

Variables and Coordinate Graphs

The bicycle was invented in 1791. Today there are over 100 million bicycles in the United States. People of all ages use bicycles for transportation and sport. Many people spend their vacations taking organized bicycle tours.

Did you know?

RAGBRAI—which stands for Register's Annual Great Bicycle Ride Across Iowa—is a week-long cycling tour across the state of Iowa. It has been held every summer since 1973. Over 7000 riders dip their back bicycle wheels into the Missouri River along Iowa's western border, spend seven days biking through Iowa's countryside and towns (following a different route every year), and end the event by dipping their front bicycle wheels into the Mississippi River on the state's eastern border.

Preparing for a Bicycle Tour

The popularity of bicycle tours gave five college students—Sidney, Celia, Liz, Malcolm, and Theo—an idea for a summer business. They would operate bicycle tours for school and family groups. They chose a route from Philadelphia, Pennsylvania, to Williamsburg, Virginia, including a long stretch along the ocean beaches of New Jersey, Delaware, and Maryland. They decided to name their business Ocean and History Bike Tours.

Investigation 1: Variables and Coordinate Graphs `5`

Tips for the Linguistically Diverse Classroom

Rebus Scenario The Rebus Scenario technique is described in detail in *Getting to Know Connected Mathematics*. This technique involves sketching rebuses on the chalkboard that correspond to key words in the story or information that you present orally. Example: some key words and phrases for which you may need to draw rebuses while discussing the "Did you know?" feature: *cycling tour* (a cluster of stick figures racing bicycles), *summer* (a sun), *back bicycle wheels into the Missouri River* (river with weeds on the bank and a bike on the bank with its rear wheel in the river), *dipping their front bicycle wheels into the Mississippi River* (different river with weeds on bank and the same bike on the bank with its front wheel in the river).

Preparing for a Bicycle Tour

At a Glance

Grouping: groups of 4

Launch

- Discuss the "Think about this!" on how far students think they can ride in one day; the purpose of the jumping jack experiment; and the functions of the jumper, counter, timer, and recorder.

- Have volunteers model the experiment.

Explore

- Make sure each student takes a turn at each of the tasks and that all four students perform the experiment.

Summarize

- Have groups share their conjectures and how they arrived at them.

- Relate the jumping jack experiment to the bike tour data in the discussion of follow-up question 2.

Assignment Choices

ACE question 5

While planning their bike tour, the five friends had to determine how far the touring group would be able to ride each day. To figure this out, they took test rides around their hometowns.

Think about this!

- How far do you think you could ride in a day?
- How do you think the speed of your ride would change during the course of the day?
- What conditions would affect the speed and distance you could ride?

To answer the questions above, you would need to take a test ride yourself. Although you can't ride your bike around the classroom, you can perform a simple experiment involving jumping jacks. This experiment should give you some idea of the patterns commonly seen in tests of endurance.

Problem 1.1

This experiment requires four people:
- a jumper (to do jumping jacks)
- a timer (to keep track of the time)
- a counter (to count jumping jacks)
- a recorder (to write down the number of jumping jacks)

As a group, decide who will do each task.

Prepare a table for recording the total number of jumping jacks after every 10 seconds, up to a total time of 2 minutes (120 seconds).

Time (seconds)	0	10	20	30	40	50	60	70	...
Total number of jumping jacks									

Here's how to do the experiment: When the timer says "go," the jumper begins doing jumping jacks. The counter counts the jumping jacks out loud. Every 10 seconds, the timer says "time" and the recorder records the total number of jumping jacks the jumper has done so far. Repeat the experiment four times so that everyone has a turn at each of the four tasks.

Answer to Problem 1.1

Student data will vary. In one class, several students started jumping at a rate of 10 jumping jacks for every 10 seconds. After 1 minute, they started to slow down slightly. Many had data entries of 107 and 108 jumping jacks for 120 seconds.

■ Problem 1.1 Follow-Up

Use your table of jumping jack data to answer these questions:

1. How did your jumping jack rate (the number of jumping jacks per second) change as time passed? How is this shown in your table?

2. What might this pattern suggest about how bike-riding speed would change over a day's time on the bicycle tour?

1.2 Making Graphs

In the jumping jack experiment, the number of jumping jacks and the time are variables. A **variable** is a quantity that changes or *varies*. You recorded your data for the variables in a table. Another way to display your data is in a coordinate graph. A **coordinate graph** is a way to show the relationship between two variables.

There are four steps to follow when you make a coordinate graph.

Step 1 *Select two variables.*

For example, for the experiment in Problem 1.1, the two variables are *time* and *number of jumping jacks*.

Step 2 *Select an axis to represent each variable.*

If time is one of the variables, you should usually put it on the *x*-axis (the horizontal axis). This helps you see the "story" that occurs over time as you read the graph from left to right. So, in a graph of the jumping jack data, time would go on the *x*-axis, and the number of jumping jacks would go on the *y*-axis (the vertical axis).

Investigation 1: Variables and Coordinate Graphs | 7

Launch

- Review how to find points on a coordinate graph.
- Read and discuss the introduction on constructing a coordinate graph.

Explore

- Circulate, helping students who are having trouble constructing their graph.
- Assign the follow-up question.

Summarize

- Have students share their graphs and answer classmates' questions.
- Display a graph and discuss the variables and scales used. Encourage students to compare this graph with the graphs they made.
- Extend the discussion to help students understand how changes in the scaling of the axes affect a graph's appearance.

Answers to Problem 1.1 Follow-Up

1. Some students will have data that show their jumping jack rate decreases as time passes. Even though the total number of jumps increases for each 10-second interval in the table, the rate decreases since the number of jumps in each 10-second interval decreases as time passes.

2. This pattern suggests that the bike-riding speed would probably decrease somewhat over a day's time.

Assignment Choices

ACE questions 1–4, 6–8, and unassigned choices from earlier problems

In many cases, you can determine which variable to assign to which axis by thinking about how the two variables are related. Does one variable *depend* on the other? If so, put the **dependent variable** on the *y*-axis and the **independent variable** on the *x*-axis. The number of jumping jacks depends on time. So, put number of jumping jacks (the dependent variable) on the *y*-axis and time (the independent variable) on the *x*-axis. You may have encountered the terms *dependent variable* and *independent variable* while doing experiments in your science classes.

Step 3 *Select a scale for each axis.*
For each axis, you need to determine the largest and smallest values you want to show on your graph and how you want to space the scale marks.

In the jumping jack experiment, the values for time are between 0 and 120 seconds, so in a graph of this data, you could label the *x*-axis (time) from 0 to 120. Since you collected data every 10 seconds, you could place marks at 10-second intervals.

The scale you use on the *y*-axis (number of jumping jacks) depends on the number of jumping jacks you did. For example, if you did 97 jumping jacks, you could label your scale from 0 to 100. Since it would be messy to put a mark for every jumping jack, you could put a mark for every 10 jumping jacks.

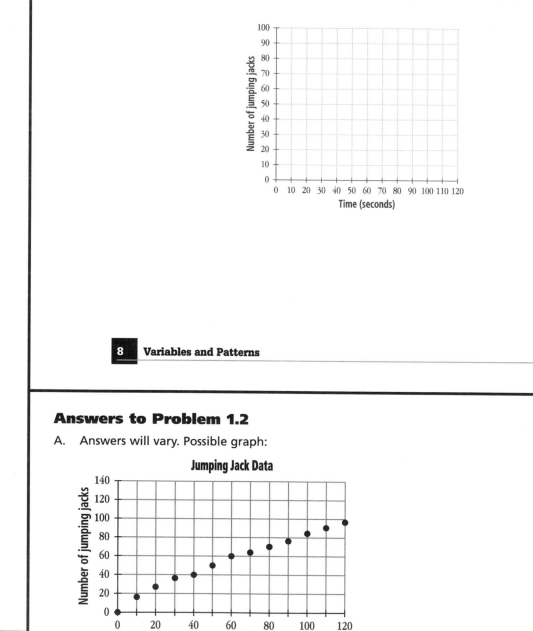

Answers to Problem 1.2

A.   Answers will vary. Possible graph:

Step 4 *Plot the data points.*

For example, suppose that at 60 seconds, you had done 65 jumping jacks. To plot this information, start at 60 on the *x*-axis (time) and follow a line straight up. On the *y*-axis (number of jumping jacks), start at 65 and follow a line straight across. Make a point where the two lines intersect. This point indicates that in 60 seconds, you did 65 jumping jacks.

Problem 1.2

A. Make a graph of your jumping jack data.

B. What does your graph show about jumping jack rate as time passes? (Another way to say this is, What does your graph show about the *relationship* between the number of jumping jacks and time?)

▦ Problem 1.2 Follow-Up

Is the relationship you found between the number of jumping jacks and time easier to see in the table or the graph? Explain your answer.

B. Answers will vary. The graph at the left shows that while the total number of jumping jacks increases over time, the number of jumps in a 10-second interval decreases over time. Be sure students understand the graph shows this because the vertical distance between adjacent points becomes less as time passes. This may be tough for students, but they will see the same concept again in the next investigation when they look at how distance changes over time.

Answer to Problem 1.2 Follow-Up

Answers will vary. Students might note that they can see the exact numbers in the table and therefore more easily see that the jumper is slowing down. Other students might prefer the visual image of the graph. The graph gives the whole picture of the data in a glance so that changes can easily be seen.

Answers

Applications

1a. See below right.

1b. Answers will vary. It is important to give students some examples of complete and thoughtful responses early in this unit so they have a sense of what is expected of them. Possible response:

Very few bags were sold before 7:00 A.M., perhaps because many people do not eat popcorn so early in the morning. But the number jumped by 12 bags between 7:00 A.M. and 8:00 A.M., when perhaps people were stopping for a snack on their way into school. The number goes up at a rate of about 5 bags an hour between 8:00 A.M. and 11:00 A.M. From 11:00 A.M. until noon it jumps to 15 bags, and 13 bags from noon to 1:00 P.M.; during these two hours perhaps people are buying lunch. No popcorn is sold from 1:00 P.M. to 2:00 P.M., and only 4 bags are sold between 2:00 P.M. and 3:00 P.M., and then the number jumps again to 12 bags from 3:00 P.M. to 4:00 P.M. Maybe people were ready for a mid-afternoon or after-school snack. During the next three hours, between 4:00 P.M. and 7:00 P.M., the number sold drops from 9 bags the first hour to 5 bags between 5:00 P.M. and 6:00 P.M. and finally dips to 4 bags sold between 6:00 P.M. and 7:00 P.M. Dinner time is probably the cause of this decrease in sales.

As you work on these ACE questions, use your calculator whenever you need it.

Applications

1. The convenience store across the street from Metropolis School has been keeping track of their popcorn sales. The table below shows the total number of bags sold beginning at 6:00 A.M. on a particular day.

a. Make a coordinate graph of these data. Which variable did you put on the *x*-axis? Why?

b. Describe how the number of bags of popcorn sold changed during the day. Explain why these changes may have occurred.

Time	Total bags sold
6:00 A.M.	0
7:00 A.M.	3
8:00 A.M.	15
9:00 A.M.	20
10:00 A.M.	26
11:00 A.M.	30
noon	45
1:00 P.M.	58
2:00 P.M.	58
3:00 P.M.	62
4:00 P.M.	74
5:00 P.M.	83
6:00 P.M.	88
7:00 P.M.	92

1a. Time should go on the *x*-axis, since the number of bags of popcorn sold depends on time. Possible graph:

Popcorn Sales

2. The graph below shows the numbers of cans of soft drink purchased each hour from a school's vending machine in one day (6 means the time from 5:00 to 6:00, 7 represents the time from 6:00 to 7:00, and so on).

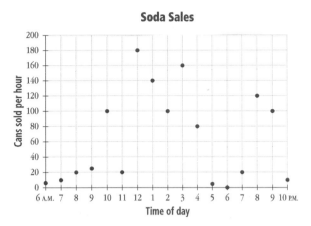

Soda Sales

a. The graph shows the relationship between two variables. What are the variables?

b. Describe how the number of cans sold changed during the day. Give an explanation for why these changes might have occured.

3. Below is a chart of the water depth in a harbor during a typical 24-hour day. The water level rises and falls with the tides.

Hours since midnight	0	1	2	3	4	5	6	7	8	9	10	11	12
Depth (meters)	10.1	10.6	11.5	13.2	14.5	15.5	16.2	15.4	14.6	12.9	11.4	10.3	10.0

Hours since midnight	13	14	15	16	17	18	19	20	21	22	23	24
Depth (meters)	10.4	11.4	13.1	14.5	15.4	16.0	15.6	14.3	13.0	11.6	10.7	10.2

2a. The two variables are time of day and the number of cans sold each hour.

2b. See page 17e.

3a. The water is deepest at 6 hours after midnight, or 6:00 A.M., with a depth of 16.2 m.

3b. The water is shallowest at noon with a depth of 10.0 m.

3c. The water depth changes most rapidly—by 1.7 meters—during each of these hours: from 2 to 3 (2 A.M.–3 A.M.), from 8 to 9 (8 A.M.–9 A.M.), and from 14 to 15 (2 P.M.–3 P.M.).

3d. See below right.

3e. Possible answer: I used 1-hour intervals on the *x*-axis because these were the time intervals given in the table. I used 2-meter intervals on the *y*-axis because it allowed all the data to be graphed on my grid paper. (Not all students will use this scale.)

a. When is the water deepest? What is the depth at that time?

b. When is the water shallowest? What is the depth at that time?

c. During what time interval does the water depth change most rapidly?

d. Make a coordinate graph of the data. Describe the overall pattern you see.

e. How did you determine what scale to use? Do you think everyone in your class used the same scale?

Connections

4. The mayor of Huntsville and her advisory board were trying to persuade a company to build a factory in the town. They told the company's owner that the population of Huntsville was growing very fast and would provide the factory with an abundant supply of skilled labor. A local environmental group protested, saying this company had a long history of air and water pollution. They tried to persuade the factory owner that the population was not increasing as fast as the mayor's group had indicated. The company hired their own investigator to research the situation. When the three parties met, each party presented a graph. The graphs are shown below and on the next page.

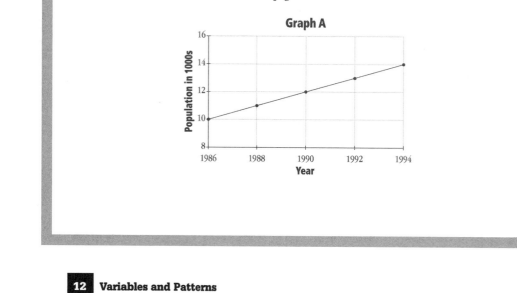

Graph A

3d. Possible answer: The data seem to be in a pattern that repeats. In the first 6 hours, the depth increases. During the next 6 hours, the depth decreases. The pattern continues for the next 12 hours.

Harbor Water Depth

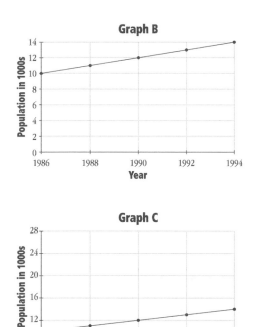

Graph B

Graph C

a. Which graph do you think was presented by the mayor? The environmentalists? The company's investigator? Explain your reasoning.

b. Is it possible that all the graphs correctly represent the population growth in Huntsville? Why or why not?

c. Describe the relationship between time and population as shown in the graphs.

4a. The mayor probably made graph A because the vertical scale starts at 8, giving the appearance of low population in 1986. The selection of interval size and spacing for the graph gives the appearance of a rapidly growing population. The investigator probably made graph B because the numbers on the vertical scale begin with 0 showing the growth from 0 to 10,000 already achieved by 1986 and a slow, steady growth thereafter. The environmental group probably made graph C because the vertical scale begins at 8, giving the appearance of a low population in 1986. The selection of interval size and spacing for the population is greater than the other graphs, yet the distance between the numbers is the same as that for graph A, giving the appearance of a population low to begin with that is growing at a very slow rate.

4b. Yes, they all show the same information, but they use different scales on the *y*-axis and different spacing between the numbers on the scale.

4c. Population is growing at a steady rate each year—it grows by about 500 people each year. This is shown on each of the graphs even though they use different scales.

5. Although Ken's points appear higher on these two graphs, he did not do more jumping jacks in 120 seconds. The scales of the two graphs are different. Andrea did about 110 jumping jacks in 120 seconds while Ken only did about 72.

6a. See below right.

6b. The range for the data is from 2 to 14, or 12 days. The median is 5 days. The mean, rounded to the nearest tenth, is 5.9 days. The mode is 3 days.

6c. Answers will vary. Some students may observe that half of the most popular tours are shorter than 5 days (using the median), and half are longer than 5 days, so a 5-day tour is the average length and should be a popular option. Other students may observe that the 3-day tour is the most preferred length (using the mode) and surmise that a 3-day trip may be a better option.

5. After doing the jumping jack experiment, Andrea and Ken compared their graphs. Because his points were higher, Ken said he did more jumping jacks than Andrea in the 120 seconds. Do you agree? Why or why not?

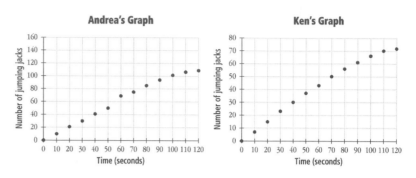

6. The operators of Ocean and History Bike Tours wanted to compare their plans with other bicycle tour companies. The bike tour they were planning would take five days, and they wondered if this might be too long or too short for people. Malcolm called 18 different companies and asked, "How many days is your most popular bike trip?" Here are the answers he received:

3, 6, 7, 5, 10, 7, 4, 2, 3, 3, 5, 14, 5, 7, 12, 4, 3, 6

a. Make a line plot of the data.

b. Find the range, median, mean, and mode of the data.

c. On the basis of this information, should Ocean and History Bike Tours change the length of the five-day trip? Explain your reasoning.

6a.

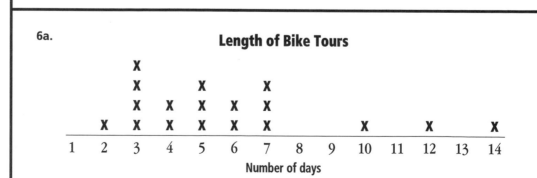

7. Which of the following graphs best represents the relationship between a person's age and height? Explain your choice. If you feel that none of the graphs shows this relationship, draw and explain your own graph.

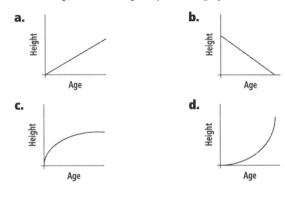

a.

b.

c.

d.

Extensions

8. The number of hours of daylight in a day changes throughout the year. We say that the days are "shorter" in winter and "longer" in summer. The following table shows the number of daylight hours in Chicago, Illinois, on a typical day during each month of the year (January is month 1, and so on).

Month	Daylight hours
1	10.0
2	10.2
3	11.7
4	13.1
5	14.3
6	15.0
7	14.5
8	13.8
9	12.5
10	11.0
11	10.5
12	10.0

7. Answers will vary. Generally speaking, over time, a person's height increases and then levels out. Hence, graph b is definitely out since it shows that height decreases over time. Graphs a, c, and d all show height increasing over time. Graph a shows a steady increase while graph c shows a sharp increase that levels off. Graph d shows just the opposite—a slow start that takes off at a certain time. Which graph makes the most sense might depend on the actual scale for the *x*-axis. For example, if we are looking at time around adolescence, then perhaps graph d makes the most sense. There may also be intervals of time in an individual's life when growth is steady as graph a indicates. If we are looking at time that spans an entire lifetime, graph c might make the most sense, since it shows that as time passes, growth levels off.

Extensions

Possible Answers

8a. Possible answer: The hours of daylight are shortest in January and December. They are longest in June. The number of hours of light changes most rapidly (by 1.5 hours) from February to March and September to October.

8b. See page 17e.

8c. See page 17e.

8d. See page 17e.

a. Describe any relationships you see between the two variables.

b. On a grid, sketch a coordinate graph of the data. Put months on the *x*-axis and daylight hours on the *y*-axis. Do you see any patterns?

c. The seasons in the Southern Hemisphere are the opposite of the seasons in the Northern Hemisphere. When it is summer in North America, it is winter in Australia. Melbourne, Australia, is about the same distance south of the equator as Chicago is north of the equator. Sketch a graph showing the relationship you would expect to find between the month and the hours of daylight in Melbourne.

January in Chicago   **January in Melbourne**

d. Put the (month, daylight) values from your graph in part c into a table.

Mathematical Reflections

In this investigation, you learned about variables. You made tables and graphs to show how different variables are related. These questions will help you summarize what you have learned:

1 In this investigation, you conducted a jumping jack experiment, collected the data in a table, and made a coordinate graph of the data. Your table and graph showed the relationship between two variables. What were the two variables? How did one variable affect the other?

2 **a.** Name some things in the world around you that vary and that can be counted or measured. Name two variables that you think are related.

b. Explain how you could make a graph to show the relationship between the two related variables from part a. How would you decide which variable should be on the *x*-axis and which should be on the *y*-axis?

Think about your answers to these questions, discuss your ideas with other students and your teacher, and then write a summary of your findings in your journal.

Tips for the Linguistically Diverse Classroom

Diagram Code The Diagram Code technique is described in detail in *Getting to Know Connected Mathematics*. Students use a minimal number of words and drawings, diagrams, or symbols to respond to questions that require writing. Example: Question 1—A student might answer this question by writing the heading *Variables*. Under this heading, the student might draw a clock (to represent time) and a stick figure doing jumping jacks. Under the clock, the student might write *independent*; under the stick figure, *dependent*.

1.1 • Preparing for a Bicycle Tour

In *Variables and Patterns*, students explore the idea of variables and how two variables change relative to each other. They look for relationships and patterns of change between two variables. In this problem, students investigate the relationship between time and the number of jumping jacks they can do.

Launch

Read aloud the information about bicycles and the yearly bicycle tour across Iowa. Encourage students to share other facts about organized bicycle tours they might know. Then continue reading about the bicycle trip that the five college students are planning. Have students share their ideas to the questions in the "Think about this!" on page 6. Students should justify their guesses about the distance they think they could ride in a day and consider ways in which their speed might vary throughout the day.

After a short class discussion, move on to the stamina experiment. Connect the bike touring and the jumping jack experiment by pointing out that both activities involve physical exertion over a period of time. This experiment works best if students are divided into groups of four. Within the group, each student has a job: performing jumping jacks, counting jumps, timing when 10 seconds has passed, and recording the number of jumping jacks completed at the end of every 10 seconds for the 2-minute time period.

For the Teacher: Timing Jumping Jacks

It is suggested that students do jumping jacks for 2 minutes. If the time limit is too short (say only 1 minute), then the jumping jack rate is not as likely to change. Two minutes has worked well in several classes. We suggest that you tell students to talk to you if they are not physically able to do the experiment. Inform everyone that if they get tired they should stop.

You may wish to have a group of four students model the experiment in order to describe and clarify the roles of each person in the group, while you emphasize the following points.

The *jumper* performs a complete jumping jack when he or she completes these three steps:

- Start with feet together and hands at sides.

- Jump, landing with legs apart and hands touching above the head.

- Jump again, returning to the starting position with feet together and hands at sides.

The *counter* counts an additional jump each time the jumper returns to the starting position.

The *timer* calls out "time" when each 10 seconds passes.

The *recorder* listens for the timer to call "time" and then writes the last number the counter called into the table.

Suggest that students make a table with the times from 10 seconds to 120 seconds listed in 10-second intervals before conducting the experiment. After the demonstration, have students perform the experiment in Problem 1.1. Remind them that they need to count and record the *total* number of jumping jacks their teammates complete after a certain time.

Explore

Students can work in groups of four to gather the data. As students work, verify their understanding of each role's function. Have each student take a turn at each task. When the group is finished, give them time to make a copy of the data for each person in their group. After students have collected and recorded the data, assign follow-up questions 1 and 2. Encourage students to discuss within their group possible explanations for what they see in their tables. Students should address the questions in the problem and consider all four data sets when answering.

For the Teacher: Saving Data

The data students collected for Problem 1.1 are used in Problem 1.2.
Be sure to have students keep a record of their own data.

Summarize

Have groups share their conjectures about rates of jumping jacks. Some groups may want to share all or part of their data on the board to help them make a point. When discussing follow-up question 2, ask what the jumping jack experiment suggests about bicycle-riding speed over time. (Usually the rate decreases as time passes.)

1.2 • Making Graphs

Problem 1.2 uses the data collected from Problem 1.1. This problem asks students to look at the jumping jack information in another way by constructing a coordinate graph.

Launch

You may wish to review coordinate graphs by asking questions such as the following:

> What does a coordinate graph look like? *(a grid with points that represent pairs of related numerical data, the x-axis representing one variable and the y-axis representing the other)*

> When do you use a coordinate graph? *(to show relationships between two variables)*

How do you locate points on a coordinate graph? *(Locate the x variable on the x-axis and draw an imaginary line perpendicular to the x-axis from that point. Repeat with the y variable. The point of intersection is the point on the coordinate graph.)*

If your students used Connected Mathematics in grade 6, remind them that these ideas were introduced in the *Data About Us* unit. After reviewing coordinate graphs, read aloud the introduction to Problem 1.2 on constructing a coordinate graph.

Explore

Have students construct graphs using their jumping jack data (either on large grid paper or on transparent grids for showing in the discussion). When students have completed their graphs, have them record their thoughts to part B and to the follow-up question.

Summarize

You might want to have a few students construct their graphs on a transparent grid to share with the class. These examples can be used to enhance student discussion. Allow students to ask why the group made their graphs as they did. Use these examples to clear up any problems students are having. Point out things done correctly. You might want to display one of the graphs and ask students these questions.

Which variable is on the *x*-axis? *(time)* Why? *(The student edition suggests that time be on the x-axis as it is the independent variable.)*

What is the smallest value on the *x*-axis? *(0)*

Some students may say the smallest value should be 10 instead of 0. This question gives you an opportunity to have students think about why 0 needs to be on the axis.

What is the largest value on the *x*-axis? *(120)*

Why is it reasonable to have the scale go from 0 to 120? *(Because that is the amount of time we spent counting jumping jacks.)*

What is the size of the interval for the *x*-axis scale? *(10 seconds)* Why is it reasonable that the interval be 10 seconds? *(Because we collected data in intervals of 10 seconds.)*

Which variable is on the *y*-axis? *(number of jumping jacks)*

What is the smallest value on the *y*-axis? *(0)* What is the largest value on the *y*-axis?

Did everyone have the same number for their largest value? Why or why not? *(Probably not, because all students do not jump at the same rate.)*

What is the size of the interval for the *y*-axis scale? *(Answers will vary although 10 will be a common interval.)* Did everyone have that size interval? Why or why not? *(Answers will vary depending on data and preference. It is not necessary for all students to have the same interval although many will.)*

What do you think would happen to this graph if the size of the intervals was changed? For example, what would happen to the graph if the *y*-axis was changed so that each interval was 5 jumping jacks instead of 10? *(The steepness of the graph would change.)*

For the Teacher: Using Different Scales

You may wish to use Transparency 1.2B or prepare a transparent grid that shows several grids using various scales. The grids below show two examples of the same data graphed using different scales.

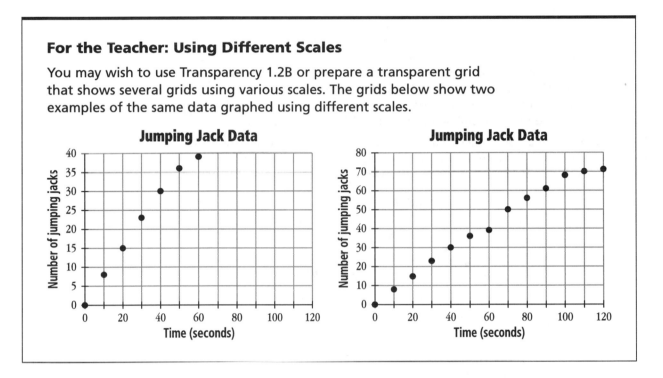

The follow-up question asks students about relationships. This is probably a new usage of this word for most students. You will want to find ways to use the word *relationship* when discussing tables and graphs in the future. Students might not have much to say about this idea so early in the unit. If no one has any comments, you may wish to model the process of looking at the relationships between variables. You might say, "In the table, I found the numbers are easy to read, and it is easy for me to use the table to calculate the number of jumps for each 10-second interval. But it is easier for me to see when the person started to slow down by looking at the graph. I see that the graph is getting less steep near the end of the time period. People were probably slowing down because they were tired."

Additional Answers

ACE Answers

Applications

2b. Because this is not a cumulative graph, some students may be confused. Unlike their graphs showing the jumping jack data, each point in this graph tells how many cans were sold during the one hour preceding that time. Possible response:

Not many cans were sold before 9:00 A.M., probably because most people do not drink soft drinks early in the morning. The number jumps to about 100 cans by 10:00 A.M., when perhaps people were ready for a mid-morning break. The number drops to around 20 cans at 11:00 A.M. At noon it jumps to about 180 cans, when some people grab a soft drink to go with their lunch. The number goes down again; at 2:00 P.M. about 100 cans were sold. Then the number jumps to about 160 cans at 3:00 P.M.; many people may be out of class on a break. The number of cans sold decreases until 6:00 P.M., when no cans were sold. Perhaps most people had already left the school. The number peaks again at 8:00 P.M. when about 120 cans were sold and drops off again until 10:00 P.M. when only about 10 cans were sold. Maybe there was some after-school activity that brought people to school at 8:00 P.M. and then the building closed at 10:00 P.M.

8b. The patterns in the graph suggest that the days are longest in June and shortest in December and January. The rate of increase of daylight hours from January to June is roughly comparable to the rate of decrease of daylight hours from June to December.

8c. Possible answer:

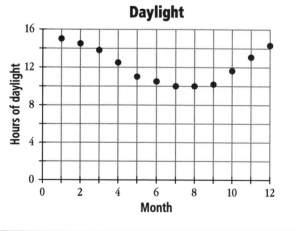

8d.

Month	1	2	3	4	5	6	7	8	9	10	11	12
Daylight hours	15	14.5	13.8	12.5	11	10.5	10	10	10.2	11.7	13.1	14.3

Graphing Change

In this investigation, prospective tour directors keep records of the distances traveled and the conditions encountered on their five-day trip. Each of these days is designed to give students a new experience with working with variables, tables, and graphs.

The data for the first four problems involves the variables time and distance. In Problem 2.1, Day 1: Philadelphia to Atlantic City, students are asked to read and make sense of data presented in a table. Students make a graph from data presented in a table in Problem 2.2, Day 2: Atlantic City to Lewes, make tables from data given in a graph in Problem 2.3, Day 3: Lewes to Chincoteague Island, and compare the tables and graphs containing like data in both problems. Students solve an open-ended problem by making a table and graph from a narrative in Problem 2.4, Day 4: Chincoteague Island to Norfolk. In Problem 2.5, Day 5: Norfolk to Williamsburg, students are asked to analyze a graph that shows the relationship between time and speed.

Mathematical and Problem-Solving Goals

- **To make sense of data given in the form of a table or a graph**

- **To read a narrative of a situation that changes over time and make a table and graph that represent these changes**

- **To read data given in a table and make a graph from the table**

- **To read data given in a graph and make a table from the graph**

- **To compare tables, graphs, and narratives and understand the advantages and disadvantages of each form of representation**

Materials		
Problem	**For students**	**For the teacher**
All	Graphing calculators, grid paper (provided as a blackline master)	Transparencies 2.1A to 2.5 (optional)
ACE	Paper cutouts of hexagons (optional; for question 12)	

Student Pages 18–35   Teaching the Investigation 35a–35k

Day 1: Phila-delphia to Atlantic City

Grouping: individuals, then pairs

Launch

- Make sure students understand that 0.5 hours means half an hour or 30 minutes.

- Discuss what it means to compare two things.

Explore

- Have students first work on the problem individually and then with a partner to create one report.

Summarize

- Share reports. Encourage students to identify patterns of change, to give possible explanations for the changes, and to compare the findings of various pairs of students.

- Discuss what variables describe the conditions affecting the riders' progress.

INVESTIGATION 2

Graphing Change

Sidney, Liz, Celia, Malcolm, and Theo found they could comfortably ride from 60 to 90 miles in one day. They used these findings, along with a map and campground information, to plan a five-day tour route. The students wondered how the route would actually work for cyclists. For example, rough winds coming off the ocean or lots of steep hills might make the trip too difficult for some riders.

The friends set off to test the proposed tour route. To make sure the trip would appeal to high school students, Sidney asked her 13-year-old brother, Tony, and her 15-year-old sister, Sarah, to come along. The five college students planned to collect data during certain parts of the trip and use their findings to write detailed reports. They could use their reports to improve their plans and to explain the trip to potential customers.

2.1 Day 1: Philadelphia to Atlantic City

The students began their bike tour near the Liberty Bell and Independence Hall in historic Philadelphia, Pennsylvania. Their goal for the first day was to reach Atlantic City, New Jersey. Sidney, Liz, Sarah, Celia, and Malcolm rode their bicycles. Theo and Tony followed along in a van with the camping gear and repair equipment. Tony recorded the distance reading on the van's trip odometer every half hour from 8:00 A.M. to 4:00 P.M. A map for the entire trip, and Tony's recordings from the first day, are given on the next page.

Assignment Choices

ACE question 9 and unassigned choices from earlier problems

Answers to Problem 2.1

Reports will vary. Below are possible answers to the three guiding questions posed in the problem.

- The riders traveled 89 miles in 8 hours.

- To find the greatest and least distances traveled, find the distance traveled each half hour. The greatest distance traveled was 10 miles between hours 0.5 and 1.0 (8:30–9:00 A.M.) and between hours 2.0 and 2.5 (10:00–10:30 A.M.). The least distance traveled was 0 miles between hours 3.0 and 4.0 (11:00–12:00).

- Noon is hour 4.0 in the table. The distance covered by noon was 47 miles. The afternoon distance was 89 – 47, or 42 miles. The riders made more progress in the first half of the day.

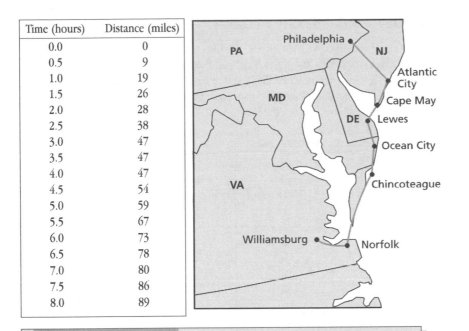

Time (hours)	Distance (miles)
0.0	0
0.5	9
1.0	19
1.5	26
2.0	28
2.5	38
3.0	47
3.5	47
4.0	47
4.5	54
5.0	59
5.5	67
6.0	73
6.5	78
7.0	80
7.5	86
8.0	89

Problem 2.1

Write a report summarizing the data Tony collected on day 1 of the tour. Describe the distance traveled compared to the time. Look for patterns of change in the data. Be sure to consider the following questions:

• How far did the riders travel in the day? How much time did it take them?

• During which time interval(s) did the riders make the most progress? The least progress?

• Did the riders go further during the first half or the second half of the day's ride?

■ Problem 2.1 Follow-Up

Describe any similarities between the jumping jack data you recorded in Problem 1.1 and the data Tony collected.

Answer to Problem 2.1 Follow-Up

Possible answer: In both data sets, the participants appear to be tiring as time passes. In the jumping jack data, people did fewer jumping jacks in the second minute than they did in the first. On the first day of the bicycle trip, the riders pedaled more miles in the first half of the day than the second.

Tips for the Linguistically Diverse Classroom

Enactment The Enactment technique is described in detail in *Getting to Know Connected Mathematics*. Students act out mini-scenes, using props, to make information comprehensible. Example: Problem 2.1—Students could enact the roles of the bicycle riders and those following in the van. A drawing of an odometer, paper, and pencils could be used as props; students could assume the roles of Theo and Tony and enact the recording of distances.

Day 2: Atlantic City to Lewes

On the second day of their bicycle trip, the group left Atlantic City and rode five hours south to Cape May, New Jersey. This time, Sidney and Sarah rode in the van. From Cape May, they took a ferry across the Delaware Bay to Lewes, Delaware. They camped that night in a state park along the ocean. Sarah recorded the following data about the distance traveled until they reached the ferry:

Time (hours)	Distance (miles)
0.0	0
0.5	8
1.0	15
1.5	19
2.0	25
2.5	27
3.0	34
3.5	40
4.0	40
4.5	40
5.0	45

At a Glance

Grouping: individuals or small groups

Launch

- Have students compare the data collected in day 2 with the data collected in day 1.
- Review the decisions required to make a coordinate graph, such as which variables and scales to use.

Explore

- Have each student make a graph.

Summarize

- Assess students' ability to make and use graphs by asking questions that can be answered using the coordinate graphs they constructed. Ask questions about the construction of the graphs and how changes in the scale affect the appearance of the graphs.
- Have students discuss the strengths and weaknesses of displaying data in graphs and tables.

Problem 2.2

A. Make a coordinate graph of the (time, distance) data given in the table.

B. Sidney wants to write a report describing day 2 of the tour. Using information from the table or the graph, what could she write about the day's travel? Be sure to consider the following questions:

- How far did the group travel in the day? How much time did it take them?
- During which time interval(s) did the riders make the most progress? The least progress?
- Did the riders go further in the first half or the second half of the day's ride?

C. By analyzing the table, how can you find the time intervals when the riders made the most progress? The least progress? How can you find these intervals by analyzing the graph?

D. Sidney wants to include either the table or the graph in her report. Which do you think she should include? Why?

Assignment Choices

ACE questions 1, 10, 11, and unassigned choices from earlier problems

Answers to Problem 2.2

A. See page 35g.

B. They traveled a total of 45 miles in 5 hours. The riders made the most progress between hours 0.5 and 1.0 and between hours 2.5 and 3.0, traveling 7 miles in each of those half-hour periods. They made the least progress from hours 3.5 to 4.5 when they did not go anywhere. We do not know what time it was when they began riding, but they covered more ground during their first 2.5 hours than their last 2.5 hours—27 miles compared with 18 miles.

C. See page 35g.

D. Students who choose the table may say that it gives exact data for a given time. Students who choose the graph may say that it shows the "picture" of all the data for the day. It is easy to see when the change in distance is great, small, or unchanged.

■ Problem 2.2 Follow-Up

1. Look at the second point on your graph as you count from the left. We can describe this point with the *coordinate pair* (0.5, 8). The first number in a **coordinate pair** is the value for the *x*-coordinate, and the second number is the value for the *y*-coordinate. Give the coordinate pair for the third point on your graph. What information does this point give?

2. Connecting the points on a graph sometimes helps you see a pattern more clearly. You can connect the points in situations in which it makes sense to consider what is happening in the intervals *between* the points. The points on the graph of the data for day 2 can be connected because the riders were moving during each half-hour interval, so the distance was changing.
   a. Connect the points on your graph with straight line segments.
   b. How could you use the line segments to help you estimate the distance traveled after $\frac{3}{4}$ of an hour (0.75 hours)?

3. The straight line segment you drew from (4.5, 40) to (5.0, 45) gives you some idea of how the ride might have gone between the points. It shows you how the ride would have progressed if the riders had traveled at a steady rate for the entire half hour. The actual pace of the group, and of the individual riders, may have varied throughout the half hour. These paths show some possible ways the ride may have progressed:

Match each of these connecting paths with the following travel notes.
   a. Celia rode slowly at first and gradually increased her speed.
   b. Tony and Liz rode very quickly and reached the campsite early.
   c. Malcolm had to fix a flat tire, so he started late.
   d. Theo started off fast. After a while, he felt tired and slowed down.

Answers to Problem 2.2 Follow-Up

1. The coordinate pair is (1, 15). This point tells us that after 1 hour the cyclists have gone 15 miles.

2. a. See page 35g.

   b. Find the location of 0.75 on the *x*-axis, midway between 0.5 and 1. Draw a perpendicular line straight up until it intersects the graph. Then draw a perpendicular line from this point to the *y*-axis. The estimated distance is the miles shown on the *y*-axis at the point of intersection, or about 11.5 miles.

3. a. ii   b. iv   c. iii   d. i

Day 3: Lewes to Chinco- teague Island

Grouping: individuals or pairs

Launch

■ Make sure students understand that the distance displayed on the *y*-axis is the miles from Lewes, *not* the total miles traveled.

■ Encourage students to find possible explanations for the changes on the graph.

Explore

■ Help students who are having difficulty making a table or identifying points.

Summarize

■ Have a couple of students share their tables.

■ Discuss whether it is appropriate to connect the points on the graph and the assumptions involving the rate of change when a straight line is used to connect points.

■ Talk about strengths and weaknesses of graphs and tables.

2.3 Day 3: Lewes to Chincoteague Island

On day 3 of the tour, the students left Lewes, Delaware, and rode through Ocean City, Maryland, which has been a popular summer resort since the late 1800s. They decided to stop for the day on Chincoteague Island, which is famous for its annual pony auction.

Did you know?

Assateague Island, located next to Chincoteague Island, is home to herds of wild ponies. According to legend, the ancestors of these ponies swam ashore from a Spanish vessel that capsized near the island in the late 1500s. To survive in a harsh environment of beaches, sand dunes, and marshes, these sturdy ponies eat saltmarsh, seaweed, and even poison ivy!

To keep the population of ponies on the island under control, an auction is held every summer. During the famous "Pony Swim," the ponies that will be sold swim across a quarter mile of water to Chincoteague Island.

Celia collected data along the way and used it to make the graph below. Her graph shows the distance the riders were from Lewes as the day progressed. This graph is different from the graph made for Problem 2.2, which represented the *total* distance traveled as the day progressed.

Day 3 Progress

Assignment Choices

ACE questions 2, 8, and unassigned choices from earlier problems

Answers to Problem 2.3

A. Answers will vary. Connecting points can help us see the changes in the data more quickly. However, straight lines would imply that the riders were traveling at a constant speed.

B. Although the format of the students' tables may vary, the information should be roughly the same depending on students' estimates of the coordinates of the points on the graph.

Time (hours)	0	0.5	1	1.5	2	2.5	3	3.5	4	4.5	5	5.5	6	6.5	7	7.5
Distance (miles)	0	7	13	22	22	30	22	31	36	48	48	56	63	72	74	81

C. Possible answer: Between hours 2 and 4, the riders needed to make a detour that brought them closer to Lewes. After the detour, they continued on to Chincoteague Island. Between hours 1.5 and 2, the riders may have taken a rest break to sightsee.

Problem 2.3

A. Would it make sense to connect the points on this graph? Explain.

B. Make a table of (time, distance) data from the information in the graph.

C. What do you think happened between hours 2 and 4? Between hours 1.5 and 2?

D. Which method of displaying the (time, distance) data helps you see the changes better, a table or a graph? Explain your choice.

■ **Problem 2.3 Follow-Up**

Use the graph to determine the total distance the riders traveled on day 3. Explain how you determined your answer.

2.4 Day 4: Chincoteague Island to Norfolk

On day 4, the group traveled from Chincoteague Island to Norfolk, Virginia. Norfolk is a major base for the United States Navy Atlantic Fleet. Malcolm and Sarah rode in the van. They forgot to record the distance traveled each half hour, but they did write some notes about the trip.

Malcolm and Sarah's Notes

- We started at 8:30 A.M. and rode into a strong wind until our midmorning break.
- About midmorning, the wind shifted to our backs.
- We stopped for lunch at a barbecue stand and rested for about an hour. By this time, we had traveled about halfway to Norfolk.
- At around 2:00 P.M., we stopped for a brief swim in the ocean.
- At around 3:30 P.M., we had reached the north end of the Chesapeake Bay Bridge and Tunnel. We stopped for a few minutes to watch the ships passing by. Since bikes are prohibited on the bridge, the riders put their bikes in the van, and we drove across the bridge.
- We took $7\frac{1}{2}$ hours to complete today's 80-mile trip.

Investigation 2: Graphing Change **23**

Day 4: Chinco-teague Island to Norfolk

At a Glance

Grouping: individuals or pairs

Launch

■ Introduce the open-ended structure of this problem. Have students identify some of the time and distance data stated in the notes.

Explore

■ Remind students to use all relevant information. Suggest they may need to revise their thinking as they work.

■ Look for students who need individual help. Ask questions requiring them to verbalize their thought processes.

Summarize

■ Have students display their tables and graphs. Invite the class to compare the displays.

■ Discuss the similarities and differences between displays and whether the displays are reasonable. Use the follow-up to have students relate their data entries to the notes.

D. Students' preferences and reasons will vary. The graph gives a quick overview of the day at a glance, but it is harder to know what the individual data points are and the actual amount of change between them. The table gives the total miles away from Lewes after a certain time in a very convenient and more exact form, but it is difficult to get a quick overview of the whole day.

Answer to Problem 2.3 Follow-Up

Assuming they only backtracked to mile 22, the total distance traveled for the day is the sum of the distance the riders are from Lewes at the end of the day plus the distance they traveled when they had to backtrack: 81 + 8 + 8, or 97 miles.

Assignment Choices

ACE questions 3, 5–7, and unassigned choices from earlier problems

Day 5: Norfolk to Williamsburg

Launch

- Discuss the variables needed to solve the problem and how they differ from or are the same as those in previous problems.

Explore

- It might be helpful to review how to read coordinates of a point. (See Problem 2.2 Follow-Up, question 3.)

Summarize

- Let groups present their tables and graphs and explain how they determined the data. Ask the class if the representations make sense.

- Have students share their responses. Make sure they understand the data in the graph.

Assignment Choices

ACE questions 4, 12, 13, and unassigned choices from earlier problems

Assessment

It is appropriate to use the check-up after this problem.

Problem 2.4

A. Make a table of (time, distance) data that reasonably fits the information in Malcolm and Sarah's notes.

B. Sketch a coordinate graph that shows the same information.

■ **Problem 2.4 Follow-Up**

Explain how you used each of the six notes to help you make your table and graph.

 Day 5: Norfolk to Williamsburg

The last stop on the Ocean and History Bike Tour was Williamsburg, Virginia. In America's colonial period, Williamsburg was the capital of Virginia. The buildings of that period have been restored so visitors can imagine what life was like there in the eighteenth century.

After the riders finished lunch, they decided to have a race. The winner would receive $50 from the tour company's first profits. Theo had an electronic speedometer on his bike. It recorded his *speed* every 10 minutes during the 90-minute race.

Theo's Speed

Answers to Problem 2.4

See page 35h.

Answer to Problem 2.4 Follow-Up

See page 35h.

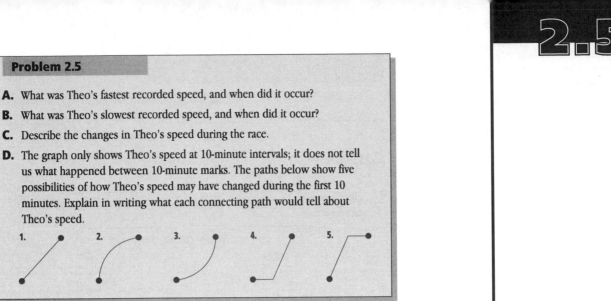

Problem 2.5

A. What was Theo's fastest recorded speed, and when did it occur?

B. What was Theo's slowest recorded speed, and when did it occur?

C. Describe the changes in Theo's speed during the race.

D. The graph only shows Theo's speed at 10-minute intervals; it does not tell us what happened between 10-minute marks. The paths below show five possibilities of how Theo's speed may have changed during the first 10 minutes. Explain in writing what each connecting path would tell about Theo's speed.

1.   2.   3.   4.   5.

■ **Problem 2.5 Follow-Up**

1. Would it be possible for the path below to represent Theo's progress between 10-minute marks? Why or why not?

2. During which 10-minute period(s) of the race did Theo's speed change the most?

Answers to Problem 2.5

A. Theo's greatest recorded speed of 20 miles per hour was recorded at 90 minutes, which was at the finish of the race.

B. The lowest recorded speed of 0 miles per hour occurred at the start of the race, 40 minutes into the race, and after the race had ended (at 100 minutes or 1 hour 40 minutes).

C. See page 35i.

D. See page 35i.

Answers to Problem 2.5 Follow-Up

See page 35i.

ACE

Answers

Applications

1a. The variables are time (measured in hours) and temperature (measured in degrees Fahrenheit).

1b. See below right.

1c. Possible answer: The high temperature for the day was around 85°F and the low temperature was around 52°F, so the difference is 85 – 52, or 33°F. (Any answer between 31°F and 36°F would be acceptable.)

1d. The temperature rose fastest between hours 1.5 and 2, 2 and 2.5, and 4 and 4.5. It fell the fastest between hours 2.5 and 3.

1e. Answers will vary, but generally it is easier to find the size of an exact increase or decrease using a table.

1f. Answers will vary, but generally it is easier to use the visual image of a graph to find the interval of greatest change since exact calculations do not need to be made.

1g. See below right.

Applications • Connections • Extensions

As you work on these ACE questions, use your calculator whenever you need it.

Applications

1. Here is a graph of temperature data collected on the students' trip from Atlantic City to Lewes.

Temperatures for Day 2

   a. This graph shows the relationship between two variables. What are they?

   b. Make a table of data from this graph.

   c. What is the difference between the day's lowest and highest temperature?

   d. During which time interval(s) did the temperature rise the fastest? Fall the fastest?

   e. Is it is easier to use the table or the graph to answer part c? Why?

   f. Is it is easier to use the table or the graph to answer part d? Why?

   g. On this graph, what information is given by the lines connecting the points? Is it necessarily accurate information? Explain your reasoning.

26 Variables and Patterns

1b. Possible table:

Time (h)	0	0.5	1	1.5	2	2.5	3	3.5	4	4.5	5
Temp. (°F)	60	52	57	60	70	80	70	65	70	80	85

1g. The lines connecting the points indicate that the temperature rose and fell at a constant rate. This is probably not true. There may be more fluctuation between any two data points than is shown with the line segments. Since it is not possible to mark every second on this graph, lines provide a general idea of the connections between the points. Although we don't know the exact connections, we can use the lines to talk about temperatures between various points on the graph.

2. Katrina's parents kept a record of her growth from her birth until her eighteenth birthday. Their data is shown in the table below.

Age (years)	Height (inches)
birth	20
1	29
2	33.5
3	37
4	39.5
5	42
6	45.5
7	47
8	49
9	52
10	54
11	56.5
12	59
13	61
14	64
15	64
16	64
17	64.5
18	64.5

a. Make a coordinate graph of Katrina's height data.

b. During which time interval(s) did Katrina have her largest "growth spurt"?

c. During which time interval(s) did Katrina's height change the least?

d. Would it make sense to connect the points on the graph? Why or why not?

e. Is it easier to use the table or the graph to answer parts b and c?

2a. See below left.

2b. between birth and age 1 (9 inches)

2c. Her height was constant from age 14 to 16 and from age 17 to 18.

2d. It would make sense to connect the points since growth occurs in the intervals between birthdays. The question of how these points should be connected, by line segments or a curve, is another point of discussion.

2e. Answers will vary. The exact change in height is easier to read from the table. However, some students may argue that the graph provides an overall picture of what is happening.

2a. Possible answer:

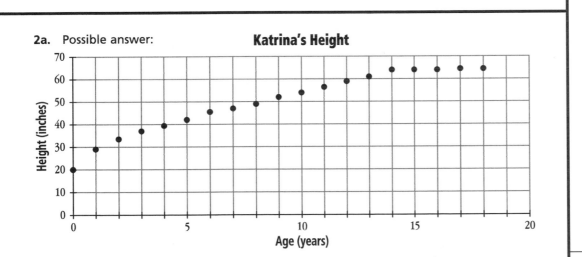

Katrina's Height

3. See page 35i.

4. The graphs share quite a few similarities, but the first graph (part a) is intended to correspond with Amanda's hunger and the second graph (part b) is intended to correspond with her happiness. The increases are quite gradual with hunger and the decreases are rather sudden when Amanda eats. The graph for Amanda's happiness shows that she can stay at the same level of happiness for a while, such as when she is having fun at basketball practice from 4 to 6.

3. Make a table and a graph of (time, temperature) data that fit the following information about a day on the road:

- We started riding at 8 A.M. The day was quite warm, with dark clouds in the sky.
- About midmorning the temperature dropped quickly to 63°F, and there was a thunderstorm for about an hour.
- After the storm, the sky cleared and there was a warm breeze.
- As the day went on, the sun steadily warmed the air. When we reached our campground at 4 P.M. it was 89°F.

4. Amanda is a student at Cartwright Middle School. She is learning how to make graphs. She made the two graphs below to show how her level of hunger and her feelings of happiness changed over the course of a day. She forgot to label the graphs.

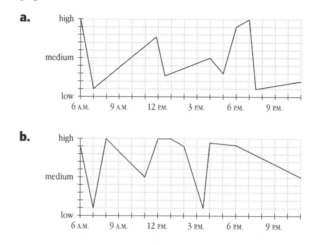

a.

b.

Here are written descriptions of how the two variables changed throughout the day. Use these descriptions to determine which graph shows the relationship between time and hunger and which graph shows the relationship between time and happiness. Explain your reasoning.

Hunger: Amanda woke up really hungry and ate a large breakfast. She was hungry again by her lunch period, which began at 11:45. After school, she had a snack before basketball practice, but she had a big appetite by the time she got home for dinner. Amanda was full after dinner and did not eat much before she went to bed.

Happiness: Amanda woke up in a good mood, but got mad because her older brother hogged the bathroom. She talked to a boy she likes on the morning bus. Amanda enjoyed her morning classes but started to get bored by lunch time. At lunch, she sat with her friends and had fun. She loves her computer class, which is right after lunch, but then didn't enjoy her other afternoon classes. After school, Amanda had a good time at basketball practice. She spent the evening washing her dog and doing other chores.

5. Here is a graph Celia drew on the bike trip.

    a. What does this graph show?

    b. Is this a reasonable pattern for the speed of a cyclist? Of the van? Of the wind? Explain each of your conclusions.

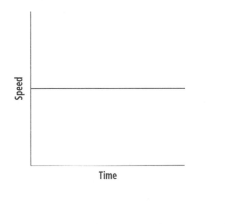

5a. The speed never changes.

5b. Answers will vary. The graph is not reasonable for a cyclist or the wind. A rider's speed can be affected by fatigue or environmental factors such as temperature, wind speed or direction, and terrain. A van could travel close to a constant speed on a flat surface with the cruise control set. The wind usually comes in gusts. It does not seem that it would remain constant over a long period of time. However, one thoughtful student answered:

"We don't know what the *scale* is. So if a small amount of space on the *y*-axis means millions and millions, then this graph is possible for the rider, the van, or the wind because their small amount of speeding up and slowing down wouldn't show up on the graph."

6a. See below right.

6b. The largest increases occur after 12 and 16 years of education. This is probably because a diploma qualifies a person for higher-paying jobs. (You may want to point out to students that these are not starting salaries. Some of these people have been in their field for a number of years. The participants of this study are people over 25.)

6c. Answers will vary. It is often easier to see changes, or jumps, in a graph, but it is easier to use a table to find the exact amount of those changes.

7a. A possible graph is shown below. It shows Ben's skill increasing rapidly at first, then more slowly.

Ben's Guitar Skill

7b. The variables are time and skill.

7c. Possible answer: hours of practice and the frequency of his lessons

---

6. The graph below shows the results of a survey of people over age 25 who had completed different levels of education. The graph shows the median salary for people with each level of education.

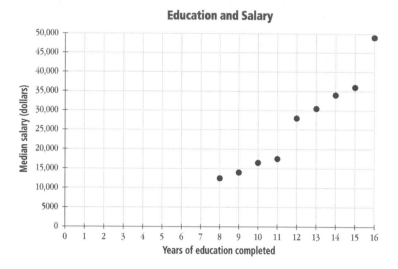

a. Make a table that shows the information in the graph.

b. After how many years of education do salaries take a big jump? Why do you think this happens?

c. Do you find it easier to answer part b by looking at the graph or your table? Explain your reasoning.

7. When Ben first started to play the electric guitar, his skill increased quite rapidly. Over time, as Ben continued to practice, he seemed to improve more slowly.

a. Sketch a graph to show how Ben's guitar-playing skill progressed over time since he began to play.

b. Your graph shows the relationship between two variables. What are they?

c. What other variables might affect the rate at which Ben's playing improves?

6a. Answers will vary but should approximate the table shown below depending on students' estimates of the coordinates of the points on the graph. (Adapted from *Statistical Abstract of the United States 1991*, published by the Bureau of the Census, Washington, D.C.)

Years of education	8	9	10	11	12	13	14	15	16
Median salary ($)	12,500	14,000	16,500	17,500	28,000	30,500	34,000	36,000	49,000

8. Think of something in your life that varies with time, and make a graph to show how it might change as time passes. Some possibilities are the length of your hair, your height, your moods, or your feelings toward your friends.

Connections

9. This table shows the percent of American children in each age group who smoke.

Age	Percent
12	1.7
13	4.9
14	8.9
15	16.3
16	25.2
17	37.2

Source: National Household Survey on Drug Abuse (1991 figures)

a. Make a bar graph of this information.

b. Based on the data, estimate the percent of 18-year-olds who smoke. Explain your reasoning.

c. What relationship does there seem to be between smoking and age? Do you think this pattern continues beyond the teenage years? Explain your reasoning.

8. Answers will vary. They may choose to graph the length of their hair. This could grow at a constant rate and then decrease rapidly when it is cut.

Connections

9a. See below left.

9b. Answers will vary. Not only is the percentage increasing, but the change between percentages is increasing. Based *only* on the data, the change from age 12 to 13 was about 3%, from 13 to 14 was 4%, from 14 to 15 was about 7%, from 15 to 16 was about 9%, and from 16 to 17 was 12%. So we could expect the change from 17 to 18 to be around 16% or that the percentage of 18-year-olds who smoke would be around 53%. Students might bring in some real-world considerations such as health hazards and peer pressure to help them make sense of this question, since 53% seems quite high.

9c. Answers will vary. The percentage of people who smoke increases with age, but this pattern could not continue because eventually we would have 100% of the population smoking, and this is not the case. Students might use other reasoning, such as smoking seems more popular with younger people than older people because older people may be more concerned about health or have less peer pressure.

9a. Possible answer:

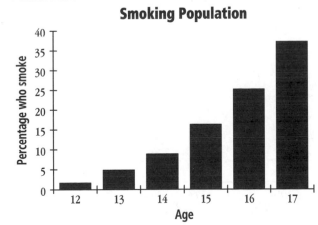

Smoking Population

10a. See below right. Note that the time scale begins at 48 seconds rather than at 0 seconds.

10b. Answers will vary. Times generally decreased, with the greatest change from 1972 to 1976. After 1976, the decreases level off with a slight increase in 1992. The best time of 48.65 seconds was earned in 1988.

10. The following table shows the winners and the winning times for the women's Olympic 400-meter dash since 1964.

Marie-Jose Perec

Year	Name	Time (seconds)
1964	Celia Cuthbert, AUS	52.0
1968	Colette Besson, FRA	52.0
1972	Monika Zehrt, E. GER	51.08
1976	Irena Szewinska, POL	49.29
1980	Marita Koch, E. GER	48.88
1984	Valerie Brisco-Hooks, USA	48.83
1988	Olga Bryzguina, USSR	48.65
1992	Marie-Jose Perec, FRA	48.83

a. Make a coordinate graph of the (year, time) information given in the table. Be sure to choose a scale that allows you to see the differences between the winning times.

b. What patterns do you see in the table and graph? For example, do the winning times seem to be rising or falling? In which year was the best time earned?

10a.

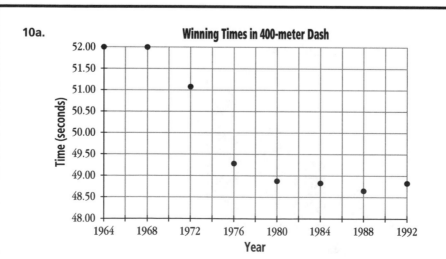

Extensions

11. The school booster club sells sweatshirts.

a. Which, if any, of the following graphs describes the relationship you expect between the price charged for each sweatshirt and the profit made? Explain your choice, or draw a new graph you think better describes this relationship. Explain your reasoning.

b. What variables can affect the club's profits?

12. The sketch below shows two bicycles—one with normal wheels, and one with wheels shaped like regular hexagons. Imagine that you put a reflector on the front wheel of each bike and then stood to the side to watch the reflector's path as the bike is ridden past you. Sketch this path:

a. If the reflector is placed at the center of each front wheel.

b. If the reflector is placed at the outer edge of each front wheel (near the tire).

Extensions

11a. Answers will vary. Students might make a reasonable argument for any of the graphs. Yet, some graphs seem to be better than others. The following arguments assume that the intersection of the *x*- and *y*-axes is point (0, 0) on all graphs. Unlike graph i, graphs ii, iii, and iv represent the idea that profit will not go up indefinitely. When you raise the price too high, some customers will stop buying. Graphs iii and iv show that there is a price that results in the maximum profit. Graph iv is a better representation since graph iii shows the unlikely event of making a profit at a very low price for each shirt. Students might draw a more detailed graph that shows a negative profit (loss) when the price is too low.

11b. Some examples are selling price, cost of sweatshirts, the location and times the booster club chooses for selling sweatshirts, and customer demand (which might depend on other variables such as income and weather).

12. See page 35j.

13. See page 35k.

13. Chelsea can pedal her bike at a steady pace for long periods of time. Think about how her speed might change if she rode in a wind that fit the pattern shown on the graph below.

   a. Sketch a coordinate graph of how Chelsea's speed would change over time if the wind were at her back (a tailwind).

   b. Sketch a coordinate graph of how Chelsea's speed would change over time if she had to ride against the wind (a headwind).

Mathematical Reflections

In this investigation, you analyzed data given in tables, graphs, and written reports. These questions will help you summarize what you have learned:

1 What are the advantages and disadvantages of a table?

2 What are the advantages and disadvantages of a graph?

3 What are the advantages and disadvantages of a written report?

Think about your answers to these questions, discuss your ideas with other students and your teacher, and then write a summary of your findings in your journal.

Possible Answers

1. A table has the advantage of giving exact figures at a glance. However, it is often hard to see patterns or trends at a glance without doing some calculations.

2. A graph has the advantage of offering a visual image from which we can quickly see patterns in the relationship between two variables. However, it is often more difficult to read exact values from a graph.

3. A written report has the advantage of giving pieces of information that cannot be contained in a graph or table, such as the reasons a certain section of a trip took longer than another section. However, in a written report it is difficult to notice patterns or trends.

Tips for the Linguistically Diverse Classroom

Original Rebus The Original Rebus technique is described in detail in *Getting to Know Connected Mathematics*. Students make a copy of the text before it is discussed. During the discussion, they generate their own rebuses for words they do not understand; the words are made comprehensible through pictures, objects, or demonstrations. Example: Question 2—key words for which students may make rebuses are *advantages* (+), *disadvantages* (–), *graph* (x- and y-axes).

2.1 • Day 1: Philadelphia to Atlantic City

In this problem, students are asked to examine data entries, to note changes, and to look for patterns.

Launch

Specific questions related to the data set have been provided to guide students. Emphasize that these questions are not the only ones to be considered when examining data and looking for patterns of change—they are simply one way of looking for patterns in this data set. As students gain experience in looking for patterns of change in data, they will gradually develop the ability to determine the relevant questions that provide the basis for their analyses. Read the introduction and Problem 2.1 aloud. Make sure students understand that 0.5 in the "Time (hours)" column means half an hour or 30 minutes. Also, students often are confused about the meaning of the word compare. You might want to ask your students what it means to compare things and what they think it means to compare in this problem.

Explore

Have students start the problem by working individually to look at the changes in the data and search for patterns of change. They should make notes, an outline, or a rough draft of a report. Have them compare their findings with a partner and together write the report. In writing the report, students will need to translate hour numbers to time of day to explain the data. Many students struggle with this. A way to help them is to ask what time of day is represented by 0 hours, 3 hours, and so on. You will also want to encourage students to think of a variety of possible explanations for the data by asking question such as "Did they eat lunch? If so, when? Where in the data does it look like this happened? Did they get tired as the day progressed?"

Summarize

Have students share their reports. After each report, ask students to identify patterns of change, give possible reasons for the changes, and note similarities and differences in the reports. Variables such as terrain, wind speed, food and rest breaks, and temperature should be mentioned as possible explanations for the data changes. If students do not use the word *variable* to describe the things that could affect the riders' speed and distance traveled, make sure that you add this word to the conversation and help them with this connection.

2.2 •
Day 2: Atlantic City to Lewes

This problem asks students to make a graph from a data set presented in a table. Doing this not only reinforces the skills of graphing but also helps students see the relationships between data presented in table form with the same information presented in graphic form. Students are also asked to look for changes in the data and to think about how these changes show up in a table and in a graph and the advantages and disadvantages of each representation.

Launch

Introduce the table displaying the data collected on day 2. Ask students to identify the similarities and the differences between this data and the data collected for day 1. (Both data sets were collected on half-hour intervals and involve the variables time and distance. A difference is that the data on day 1 was collected over an eight-hour period while it was collected for a five-hour period on day 2.)

Read Problem 2.2 with your students. You may wish to review the decisions needed to make a graph of the data. These decisions include which variables to graph, which variable to put on each axis, and what a reasonable scale for each axis might be. Using the ideas presented in Investigation 1, students should be able to explain that time is usually put on the *x*-axis. This allows the graph to tell a story of how a variable changes over time as we read from left to right.

Explore

Have students work individually or in small groups. If they work in groups, have each student make a graph. This will allow you to see who is still having difficulties with this type of graphing by the work each student does and how much each depends on members in the group to help do this exercise. Students who finish early can start on the follow-up questions.

Summarize

Display Transparency 2.2C, showing the graph of the data for day 2. Have students identify the scales used on this graph and explain their importance to the graph. If students have not labeled their graphs, have them do so at this time. Continue the discussion on coordinate graphs by asking students the following questions.

> What variable is displayed on the *x*-axis? *(time)* Why? *(Time is usually put on the x-axis so that the graph tells a story of how a variable changes over time as we read from left to right. Also, it is the independent variable and thus should go on the x-axis.)*
>
> What is the smallest value that needs to be located on the *x*-axis? *(0)*
> What is the greatest value that needs to be located on the *x*-axis? *(5)*
>
> Why is it reasonable to have the size of the interval for the *x*-axis be 0.5 hours? *(The data was collected on half-hour intervals.)*
>
> Which variable is displayed on the *y*-axis? *(distance)*
>
> What is the smallest value that needs to be located on the *y*-axis? *(0)*
> What is the greatest value that needs to be located on the *y*-axis? *(45)*
>
> What is the size of the interval for the *y*-axis on this graph? *(5 miles)*
> Did anyone have an interval for the *y*-axis other than 5 units? *(If yes, have students share and explain why this size is reasonable. Ask how this new scale affects the appearance of the graph.)*

Have students share their answers to the remaining questions in the problem. Part D asks students to think about the strengths and weaknesses of the table and graph representations. For example, a graph shows the sizes of changes in the data at a glance but does not pinpoint exact numerical changes, while a table can be better for analyzing exact changes in the data although it does not always show the sizes of the changes at a glance.

Discuss the follow-up questions. These questions are intended to review naming and locating points on a graph and to start a conversation about when and how to use line segments to connect points on a graph.

Question 2b requires students to think about how data can be extracted from a graph. Ask students what it means if two points are connected with a line segment and what must happen for that to make sense.

When line segments are used to connect points, an assumption is made that the change between one data point and another happens at a constant rate. Question 3 introduces the idea that the rate of change does not have to be constant between two data points. This is a difficult question for many students. It is worth spending time discussing these ideas if students seem ready to face these issues at this time. (A similar question is raised in Problem 2.5.) When matching graphs i–iv with statements a–d, students may question why statement a does not correspond to graph iii and why statement d does not correspond to graph iv. You may wish to emphasize that a horizontal line in these graphs means that the rider is not increasing distance and therefore is not moving at all. For graph iv, some students ask "Why does the line go on if they are not riding?" You may find it helpful to emphasize that even though the person is not riding, time continues to go on; hence, the line gives us sensible information, such as how long the rider was stopped.

2.3 • Day 3: Lewes to Chincoteague Island

This problem gives the data for day 3 in graphic form. The questions ask for interpretation of the graph and for the creation of a data table.

Launch

Read the introduction with your students. Have them examine the graph. Call attention to the change in distance between 2.5 and 3 hours and ask students what the decrease means. (The riders backtracked—making them closer to Lewes.) Students may need to be reminded that this graph shows the distance *from* Lewes rather than the total distance traveled. Encourage students to explain what might have happened to make the riders reduce their distance from Lewes. (Construction caused a detour, someone lost something and they all went back to search for it, they missed a turn and had to turn around, and so on.) Read Problem 2.3 with your students.

Explore

Have students work individually or in pairs to complete the questions. If they work in pairs, make sure each student records answers to the questions. If students are having difficulty making a table, ask which two variables are being represented on the graph. Then ask what role variables play when making a table. If they don't know, have them look at the table given to them for Problem 2.2 and the graph they constructed for that problem. These students and others having difficulty identifying and interpreting data points from the graph may find it helpful to review the tables and graphs in Problem 2.2. For students finishing early, you may wish to have them make their table on a transparency to share during the summary.

Summarize

Part A in the problem again raises the issue of connecting the points on a graph. This connects back to ideas discussed in the follow-up questions to Problem 2.2. This question keeps students thinking about when it makes sense to connect the points on a graph. For graphs for which it is appropriate to connect the points, we want to help students understand that connecting points could help us see the changes in the data more quickly. We also need to realize that we are making assumptions about distance increasing at a constant speed when we connect two points with a line. Have students share their explanations for why the points should be connected. Ask how they might connect the points and what it means if they connect the points with a straight line segment.

Have a couple of students share their table with the class. If some of your students are still struggling with this, ask the presenters to explain how they created their table. If all students were able to do this with no problems, move on.

In part D, students choose which display of information they prefer and explain why. The class conversation needs to include the strengths and weaknesses of each form. (The graph gives a quick overview of the day at a glance, but it is harder to find what the individual data points are and the actual amount of change between points. The table gives the total miles away from Lewes by a certain time in a very convenient and more exact form, but you can't get a quick overview of the whole day.)

The follow-up is a computation problem and can be asked after going over the parts of the problem. Make sure someone explains why the total distance traveled for the day is not 81 (or 82) but is the sum of $81 + 8 + 8$, or 97 miles.

2.4 • Day 4: Chincoteague Island to Norfolk

In this problem students use narrative notes to make a table and a graph. This problem is very different from what they have been doing because it is so open-ended.

Launch

Read the introduction and Problem 2.4 with your students. You may wish to help them make sense of the problem by asking the following questions.

> What are the two variables that you will use for the table and the graph? *(time and distance)* What would you choose for your time intervals? *(A common suggestion is a half hour because all the time/distance tables done in this investigation had a half-hour interval.)*

> At 0 hours what is the distance traveled? *(0 miles)* How do you know? *(Because at 0 hours you are just about to start the day's travel and have not gone anywhere yet.)*

> At 7.5 hours what is the distance traveled? *(80 miles)* How do you know? *(The last note states that the total distance traveled for the day, at the end of the 7.5 hours, was 80 miles.)*

What other data points in the table would be easy to complete based on the set of notes? *(At approximately noon, or 3.5 hours into the trip, riders had traveled about half the total distance, or 40 miles.)*

Encourage students to come up with their own data based on the constraints given in "Malcolm and Sarah's Notes" to help them complete the problem.

Explore

Have students work Problem 2.4 individually or in pairs. If they work with a partner, make sure each student makes a table and a graph. Because this question is so open-ended, many solutions are possible. You may wish to have students use large sheets of paper to make their final tables and graphs. These can be displayed for comparison during the summary. Some students may find it helpful to include the actual time of day on these representations to assist them in answering the follow-up.

Be sure students are using all the relevant information given to create their data table and graph. They will probably need to use trial-and-error methods to make their data satisfy all the constraints. For students who struggle, you may need to ask questions about each time listed in their table.

Summarize

Have students share their tables and graphs. Ask the class to look over all the displays and check for similarities and differences among them. Ask them if anyone's data seem unreasonable and why. Let that person respond to the challenge or agree with the person and change the data entries. The students' tables and graphs will be different but should share these common characteristics:

If reported in half-hour segments, there will be 16 data entries. The total distance must be 80 miles. The early morning's progress should be slower than the rest of the day because of the wind. There are three breaks, morning, lunch, and one at 2:00 P.M. (or from hours 5.5–6.0). When the riders load their cycles in the van to cross the Chesapeake Bay Bridge and Tunnel, we might assume they will cover a greater distance in a shorter time than when they were pedaling.

2.5 • Day 5: Norfolk to Williamsburg

This day's graph records time and speed (the rate) rather than time and distance. Theo's bike speedometer shows the rider's speed and records it every 10 minutes.

Launch

Read the problem aloud. To help students understand what the variables in this problem represent and to help them interpret the graph, ask the following questions.

What are the variables for the graph? *(time and speed)*

How are the variables in this graph different from the variables in the graphs for Problems 2.3 and 2.4? *(For those two problems, the variables were time and distance. In this problem, time and speed are the variables.)*

What does speed mean and how is it measured? *(Speed refers to how fast or slow something is moving. This rate is measured by the distance traveled in a set time.)*

In this problem, speeds are measured in miles per hour. What does that mean? *(It tells the distance that can be traveled in one hour.)*

What does it mean when there is a large vertical change between points? *(A large increase or decrease in the speed.)*

If two points are the same height, right next to each other vertically as you read the graph from left to right, what does that mean? *(The rider was traveling at a constant speed, or the rider was traveling at the same speed at those two intervals.)*

Explore

Have students work in pairs with each person recording a solution to the problem. If students are struggling with part D, encourage them to look back at their notes and review the discussion from question 3 of Problem 2.2 Follow-Up.

Summarize

Have students share their responses to parts A–C. You may wish to discuss possible reasons for the changes in Theo's speed (for example, changes in terrain, pacing himself for the spurt at the end, and so on). For part D, have several students share their explanations. Ask other students to explain why they think the explanations are or are not reasonable. What you want to look for is whether students are interpreting the graph, understanding what they are looking at, and describing changes in speed (not distance).

Additional Answers

Answers to Problem 2.2

A.

C. Progress can be determined by comparing the change in the value of the *y* variable for two points. Progress in the table can be determined by subtracting each entry from the entry below it in the "Distance" column and then comparing the differences. The most progress is made when this difference is the greatest, and the least progress is made when this difference is the least. Progress in the graph can be determined either by estimating the *y* value for each point and comparing the differences between pairs of adjacent points or by visually comparing the change in vertical increase.

Answers to Problem 2.2 Follow-Up

2. a.

Answers to Problem 2.4

A. Possible answer:

Time (hours)	Distance (miles)
0	0
0.5	3
1.0	5
1.5	8
2.0	18
2.5	25
3.0	33
3.5	40
4.0	40
4.5	40
5.0	46
5.5	52
6.0	52
6.5	59
7.0	65.5
7.5	80

B. Answers will vary. A graph of the data in part A is given.

Chincoteague Island to Norfolk

Answer to Problem 2.4 Follow-Up

Possible answer: I used the notes from Malcolm and Sarah to make a table first. I decided to use half-hour intervals, because all the tables and graphs in this investigation used that size time interval. Using the information that the trip started at 8:30 (first note) and that they traveled for 7.5 hours, I filled in the time column of my table. I also could fill in the distance value to match the last time entry because the last note says they traveled 80 miles. The next note I used was the third one, which stated that the stop for lunch was about an hour and that they had traveled about halfway. I decided that noon was a reasonable time for lunch (3.5 hours into the trip) and 40 would be the travel distance for that time because it is halfway. After that I used notes 1 and 2 to spread out the first 40 miles of the trip and notes 4 and 5 to spread out the last 40 miles of the trip. To make the graph, I put time on the *x*-axis and distance on the *y*-axis and plotted the data points from my table.

Answers to Problem 2.5

C.   Possible answer: Theo's speed increased quickly so that after 20 minutes his recorded speed is 17.5 miles per hour. For the next 20 minutes he seemed to slow down and came to a stop. He then increased his speed and rode faster as he neared the finish.

D.   1.   Theo traveled at a constantly increasing speed.
     2.   Theo increased his speed rapidly but then slowed his rate of increase.
     3.   Theo started slowly but then increased his rate of speed at a rapid rate.
     4.   Theo started late and then traveled at a constantly increasing speed.
     5.   Theo traveled at a constantly increasing speed, then maintained a certain speed.

Answers to Problem 2.5 Follow-Up

1.   No, because it is not possible to reach a certain speed instantaneously on a bike. The increase must be over a time interval so the cyclist can build speed.

2.   Theo's speed changed by 15 miles per hour over three 10-minute intervals, from 0–10 minutes, from 30–40 minutes, and from 40–50 minutes. (Some students may mention that Theo's speed decreased by 20 miles per hour in the last 10 minutes shown on the graph [from 90–100 minutes], but this was after the race.)

ACE Answers

Applications

3.   Answers will vary, but the graphs should show that it was warm at 8:00 in the morning, decreasing rapidly to 63°F by midmorning, and staying constant for about an hour. After this, the temperature increases until it reaches 89°F at 4:00 P.M.

Time (hours)	Temperature (°F)
0	76
1	77
2	63
3	63
4	78
5	80
6	83
7	86
8	89

A Day on the Road

Extensions

12a. On the bike with circular wheels, the reflector will remain the radius distance from the pavement if the reflector is in the center of the wheel.

reflector's path _____

ground _____

The reflector in the center of the hexagonal wheel will bump up and down as the wheel is pushed up onto a vertex and then down on to the flat part of each of the **6 sides.**

reflector's path

ground _____

12b. On the bike with circular wheels, the path would look like the first picture below. The bike with hexagonal wheels would create a path similar to the second picture below.

reflector's path —→
ground

reflector's path —→
ground

For the Teacher: Thinking About Hexagonal Wheels

The hexagonal wheels will probably be difficult for students to visualize. To help them think about this problem they can use paper cutouts of hexagons to trace the path of the reflector with the rotation of the wheel. The paper cutout allows them to punch a hole in the center of the shape to represent the center of the tire.

13. The two graphs will be mirror images around a steady speed.

13a. Possible answer:

13b. Possible answer:

Analyzing Graphs and Tables

In this investigation students consider some financial questions concerning running Ocean and History Bike Tours. The introduction asks students to think about expenses, the price charged, and an acceptable profit for the tour directors. The four problems in the investigation present various decisions that need to be made: Problem 3.1, Renting Bicycles, involves a decision about bicycle rental cost; Problem 3.2, Finding Customers, relates to the price of the tour; Problem 3.3, Predicting Profit, shows the relationship between the number of customers and profit; and Problem 3.4, Paying Bills and Counting Profits, involves looking for patterns to calculate total costs and profit. These problems ask students to make decisions by interpreting and comparing information presented in tables and graphs.

Mathematical and Problem-Solving Goals

- **To change the form of representation of data from tables to graphs and vice versa**

- **To search for patterns of change**

- **To describe situations that change in predictable ways with rules in words for predicting the change**

- **To compare forms of representation of data**

Materials		
Problem	For students	For the teacher
All	Graphing calculators, grid paper (provided as a blackline master)	Transparencies 3.1A to 3.4B (optional)

Student Pages 36–48   Teaching the Investigation 48a–48m

Analyzing Graphs and Tables

In this investigation, you will continue to use tables and graphs to compare information and make important decisions. Using tables, graphs, and words to represent relationships is an important part of algebra.

Coming up with the idea for Ocean and History Bike Tours was only the first step for the five friends in starting their business. They have other important plans to make as well. Many of these plans involve questions about money.

- What will it cost to operate the tours?
- How much should customers be charged?
- What profit will be left when all the bills are paid?

To answer these questions, the five business partners decided to do some research. They wanted to plan carefully so they would end up with a profit after they had paid all their expenses.

Think about this!

- With your classmates, make a list of the things the tour operators will have to provide for their customers. Estimate the cost of each item per customer.

- How much do you think customers would be willing to pay for the five-day tour?

- Based on your estimates of costs and possible income, will the partners earn a profit?

3.1 Renting Bicycles

The tour operators decided to rent bicycles for their customers rather than having customers bring their own bikes. They called two bike shops and asked for estimates of rental fees.

Rocky's Cycle Center sent a table of weekly rental fees for various numbers of bikes.

Number of bikes	5	10	15	20	25	30	35	40	45	50
Rental fee	$400	535	655	770	875	975	1070	1140	1180	1200

Adrian's Bike Shop sent a graph of their weekly rental fees. Since the rental fee depends on the number of bikes, they put the number of bikes on the *x*-axis.

Adrian's Bike Shop Fees

Problem 3.1

A. Which bike shop should Ocean and History Bike Tours use? Explain your choice.

B. Explain how you used the information in the table and the graph to make your decision.

Answers to Problem 3.1

A. For 35 or fewer bikes the best value is at Adrian's Bike Shop; for more than 35 bikes it is at Rocky's Cycle Center. If students calculate the exact amounts, assuming that each bike in the table interval rents for the same amount, the cutoff point is 37 bikes.

B. Answers will vary. By graphing both sets of data on a single grid, students can see that the point at which the costs are the same is where the graphs cross. One can infer that values closer to the bottom of the graph at a particular point represent lower cost. Or they can make a table for the graph by first choosing an easy value to read, such as 20 bikes for $600. Then they can find that renting one bike costs $30; thus, by multiplying any number of bikes by 30, they can complete the table.

Renting Bicycles

Grouping: individuals, then pairs

Launch

■ Have students discuss the "Think about this!" Define *income* and *profit* if necessary.

■ Review how to read the table and the graph.

Explore

■ Have students work on the problem individually and then share ideas in pairs.

■ Help students who cannot discern that the number of bikes is the most important factor.

Summarize

■ Discuss the difficulties in comparing the two data sets and the patterns in the two sets.

■ Talk about the follow-up questions.

Assignment Choices

ACE questions 3, 4, and unassigned choices from earlier problems

Launch

- Discuss and analyze the partners' market research.

Explore

- Have students work individually to complete the graph, then in pairs to finish the problem and follow-up.

- Circulate and encourage students to describe what happens to the number of customers as price increases.

Summarize

- Discuss students' reasons for choosing the variables for the *x*-axis and *y*-axis, and talk about what happens when the variables are reversed.

- Discuss students' conclusions about the price to be charged.

- Focus on students' understanding of how changes appear in tables and in graphs when reviewing follow-up question 2.

Assignment Choices

ACE questions 7–9 and unassigned choices from earlier problems

■ **Problem 3.1 Follow-Up**

1. In the graph from Adrian's Bike Shop, would it make sense to connect the points with a line? Why or why not?
2. How much do you think each company would charge to rent 32 bikes?
3. Recognizing patterns and using patterns to make predictions are important mathematical skills. Look for patterns in the table and graph on page 37. For each display, describe in words the pattern of change in the data.
4. Based on the patterns you found in part 3, how can you predict values that are not included in the table or graph?

3.2 Finding Customers

Sidney, Liz, Celia, Malcolm, and Theo had a route planned and a bike shop chosen. Now they needed customers. They had to figure out what price to charge so they could attract customers and make a profit.

To help set a price, the partners did some market research. They obtained a list of people who had taken other bicycle tours and asked 100 of them which of the following amounts they would be willing to pay for the Ocean and History Bike Tour: $150, $200, $250, $300, $350, $400, $450, $500, $550, $600. The results are shown in the table.

Tour price	Number who would be customers at this price
$150	76
200	74
250	71
300	65
350	59
400	49
450	38
500	26
550	14
600	0

Answers to Problem 3.1 Follow-Up

1. No, because one can only rent whole numbers of bikes. (Note: This question is intended to help students realize an important difference between graphs with discrete variables and those with continuous variables. Speed and time are continuous variables, and it makes sense to connect the points since a fraction of a minute is possible. Bikes and cost are discrete variables. It would not make sense to rent part of a bicycle.)

2. See page 48g.

3. See page 48g.

4. See page 48g.

Problem 3.2

A. If you were to make a graph of the data, which variable would you put on the *x*-axis? Which variable would you put on the *y*-axis? Explain your choices.

B. Make a coordinate graph of the data on grid paper.

C. Based on your graph, what price do you think the tour operators should charge? Explain your reasoning.

■ Problem 3.2 Follow-Up

1. The number of people who said they would take the tour depended on the price. How does the number of potential customers change as the price increases?

2. How is the change in the number of people who said they would go on the tour shown in the table? On the graph?

3.3 Predicting Profit

Based on the results of their survey, the tour operators decided to charge $350 per person for the tour. Of course, not all of this money would be profit. To estimate their profit, they had to consider the expenses involved in running the tour. Sidney estimated these expenses and calculated the expected profit for various numbers of customers. She made the graph below to present her predictions to her partners. Since the profit depends on the number of tour customers, she put the number of customers on the *x*-axis.

Estimated Tour Profits

Launch

■ Have students explain the purpose of the graph and the relationship being represented.

Explore

■ Have students work in pairs to solve the problem.

Summarize

■ Have students give their answers to parts A and B and describe the methods used to solve them.

■ Make up a new data set on profit and graph it. Then compare the lines to answer part D.

■ Have students use the pattern from part C to write the description in the follow-up question.

Answers to Problem 3.2

A. Independent variables such as price go on the *x*-axis, and dependent variables such as number of customers go on the *y*-axis.

B. See page 48g.   **C.** See page 48g.

Answers to Problem 3.2 Follow-Up

1. The number of customers decreases as the price increases. Since the graph is not a straight line, the decrease in the number of customers is not constant for each $50 price increase. The way the graph is curved shows that customers are less likely to drop out at a $50 increase when the tour price is low than when it is high.

2. See page 48h.

Assignment Choices

ACE questions 5, 6, and unassigned choices from earlier problems

Paying Bills and Counting Profits

Grouping:
small groups

Launch

■ With students, read the introduction and the problem,
being sure students understand that the cost of $700
for the van rental is the same
for each tour.

Explore

■ Have students make their
own table first. Then have
them work in groups of two
or three to look for and
describe patterns in the table.

Summarize

■ Complete the entries for
the table.

■ Use words to write short
summaries of the patterns
or rules students discovered
in the table.

■ For each rule offered, test
it by generating one of the
rows.

Assignment Choices

ACE questions 1, 2, 10,
and unassigned choices
from earlier problems

Problem 3.3

Study the graph on the previous page.

A. How much profit will be made if 10 customers go on the tour? 25 customers?
40 customers?

B. How many customers are needed for the partners to earn a $200 profit?
A $500 profit? A $600 profit?

C. How does the profit change as the number of customers increases? How is
this pattern shown in the graph?

D. If the tour operators reduced their expenses but kept the price at $350, how
would this change the graph?

■ **Problem 3.3 Follow-Up**

In the profit graph, points at the intersection of two grid lines, such as (20, 300) and
(40, 600), are easy to read. Use the "easy to read" points to figure out what the profit
would be if only 1 customer went on the tour. How about 2 customers? 3 customers?
100 customers? Describe, in words, the estimated profit for any number of customers.

3.4 Paying Bills and Counting Profits

Sidney was nervous about the partners using her rough estimates to make important
decisions. She decided to look more carefully at the company's expected costs and the
resulting profit. She found that although the trip would bring in $350 from each rider, it
would have operating costs of $30 for each person's bike rental, $125 for each person's
food and camp costs, and $700 per tour to rent the van for the trip. Sidney put her
estimated cost and income data in a table. Here is the start of her table:

Number of customers	Income	Bike rental	Food and camp costs	Van rental
1	$350	$30	$125	$700
2	700	60	250	700
3				
4				
5				
6				
7				
8				
9				
10				

Answers to Problem 3.3

A. Profit for 10 customers: $150; for 25 customers: $375; for 40 customers: $600

B. Customers for profit of $200: at least 14; for profit of $500: at least 34; for profit
of $600: 40

C. The profit increases as the number of customers increases. This is shown on the
graph by a steady rise in the line of points.

D. If the tour operators reduce expenses, they will have more profit. Suppose they
made a profit of $20 per person. The profit graph would look similar but rise faster
(10 customers = $200, 20 customers = $400, 50 customers = $1000).

Answer to Problem 3.3 Follow-Up

See page 48h.

Problem 3.4

A. Copy Sidney's table. Complete it to give information about income and estimated costs for up to 10 customers.

B. How does the income column change as the number of customers increases? Explain how you can use this relationship to calculate the income for any number of customers.

C. Add and complete a column for "Total cost" (including bike rental, food and camp costs, and van rental) to your table. How does the total cost change as the number of customers increases? Describe how you can calculate the total cost for any number of customers.

D. Add and complete a column for "Profit." What profit would be earned from a trip with 5 customers? 10 customers? 25 customers?

▤ Problem 3.4 Follow-Up

1. What other patterns of change do you see in the table?

2. What is the least number of customers needed for the tour to make a profit?

3. What do you think is the least number of customers needed to make it worthwhile for the students to run the tour? Explain your answer.

Answers to Problem 3.4

A. See page 48h.

B. The income increases $350 for each customer. To find income for any number of riders, multiply $350 times the number of riders.

C. The total cost increases by $155 with each new person added to the tour. One way to find the total cost for any number of riders is to add $155 times the number of riders to the cost of renting the van.

D. See page 48h.

Answers to Problem 3.4 Follow-Up

See page 48i.

Answers

Applications

1a. See page 48i.

1b. Since it does not make sense to talk about fractional parts of campsites, a line connecting the points would represent information that does not make sense. (Note: It is important to realize this, but that does not mean a graph is "wrong" if the points are connected to see the pattern more clearly.)

1c. The total fee increases by $12.50 for each additional campsite. This is shown by the line going up as we read from left to right. The values on the "Fee" axis increase 12.5 for each increase of 1 on the "Number of campsites" axis.

2a. See page 48j.

2b. Like the campground fee data, the "jump" is the same for any number of campers (or campsites needed). Hence, the graph for both would lie on a straight line. Both have constant intervals although the amounts differ.

3a. See page 48j.

As you work on these ACE questions, use your calculator whenever you need it.

Applications

1. This table shows the fees charged for campsites at one of the campgrounds on the Ocean and History Bike Tour:

Number of campsites	1	2	3	4	5	6	7	8
Total campground fee	$12.50	25.00	37.50	50.00	62.50	75.00	87.50	100.00

a. Make a coordinate graph of these data.

b. Would it make sense to connect the points on your graph? Why or why not?

c. Using the table, describe the pattern of change you find in the total campground fee as the number of campsites needed increases. How is this pattern shown in your graph?

2. A camping-supply store rents camping gear for $25 per person.

a. Using increments of 5 campers, make a table showing the total rental charge for 0 to 50 campers. Make a coordinate graph of these data.

b. Compare the pattern of change in your table and graph with patterns you found in the campground fee data in question 1. Describe the similarities and differences between the two sets of data.

3. The tour partners need to rent a truck to transport camping gear, clothes, and bicycle repair equipment. They checked prices at two truck rental companies.

a. East Coast Trucks charges $4.25 for each mile a truck is driven. Make a table of the charges for 0, 25, 50, 75, 100, 125, 150, 175, 200, 225, 250, 275, and 300 miles.

b. Philadelphia Truck Rental charges $200 for a week, or any part of a week, and an additional $2.00 for each mile a truck is driven. Make a table of the charges for renting a truck for five days and driving it 0, 25, 50, 75, 100, 125, 150, 175, 200, 225, 250, 275, and 300 miles.

c. On one coordinate grid, plot the charge plans for both rental companies. Use a different color to mark each company's plan.

d. Based on your work in parts a–c, which truck rental company do you think would be the best deal for the partners?

4. Dezi's family just bought a VCR. Dezi's mom asked him to research rental prices at local video stores. Source Video has a yearly membership package. The manager gave Dezi this table of prices:

Source Video Membership/Rental Packages

Number of videos rented	0	5	10	15	20	25	30
Total cost	$30	35	40	45	50	55	60

Extreme Video does not have a membership package. Dezi made the graph below to show how the cost at Extreme Video is related to the number of videos rented.

Video Rentals from Extreme Video

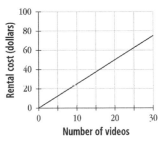

3b. See page 48j.

3c. See page 48k.

3d. If the truck is driven for less than about 89 miles, East Coast Trucks is the firm to use. If it is driven more than 89 miles, Philadelphia Truck Rental is the better choice.

4a. See page 48k.

4b. Possible answer: On the graph, the two lines cross at 20 videos. This tells us that if we rent 20 videos, the price will be the same for both stores. For fewer than 20 videos, Extreme Video is the best value. For more than 20 videos, Source Video is cheaper.

4c. Possible answer: Both costs graph as straight lines. To rent videos from Source Video, you pay $30 plus $1 for each video you rent because Source Video has a $30 membership fee plus a dollar for each video rented. Since Extreme Video has no initial fee, each video costs $2.50 to rent, so video rental is $2.50 times the number of videos rented.

Connections

5a–c. graph b; Graph a shows that Jamie has $25 in savings and never adds to it. Graphs b and c show how his savings would build over time; after 7 months, he would have $150. It is what happens during the months that makes these two graphs different. Jamie makes only one deposit of $25 at the end of the month so total savings jumps $25 and then remains constant until the end of the next month when it jumps $25 again. This is represented by graph b.

a. If both video stores have a good selection of movies, and Dezi's family plans to watch about two movies a month, which video store should they choose?

b. Write a paragraph explaining to Dezi how he could decide which video store to use.

c. For each store, describe the pattern of change relating the number of videos rented to the cost.

Connections

5. This summer Jamie is going to Washington, D.C., to march in a parade with his school band. He plans to set aside $25 at the end of each month to use for the trip. Which of the following graphs shows how Jamie's savings will build as time passes?

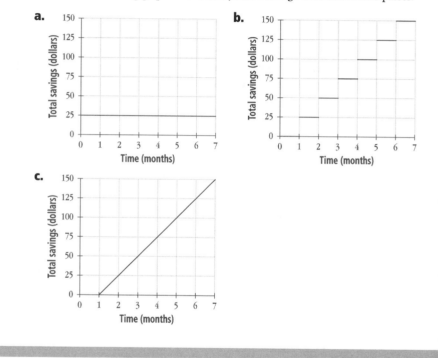

6. Jacy works at a department store on the weekends. This graph represents Jacy's parking expenses. Describe what the graph tells you about the costs for the parking garage Jacy uses.

Parking Costs

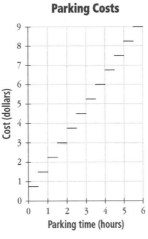

7. Recall that the area of a rectangle is its length times its width.

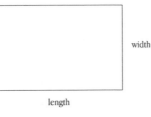

width

length

a. Make a table of the different whole-number values for the length and width of a rectangle with an area of 24 square meters.

b. Make a coordinate graph of your data from part a. Put length on the *x*-axis and width on the *y*-axis.

c. Describe what happens to the width as the length increases.

6. The graph shows that Jacy spends $0.75 to park for anything less than or equal to the first half hour. Once she passes the half-hour mark, the price jumps by another $0.75 and so on. The price is $0.75 per half hour with any fraction of a half hour rounded up. So, if she parks for 1.2 hours, she pays for three half hours at $0.75 each.

7a.

Width (meters)	Length (meters)
24	1
12	2
8	3
6	4
4	6
3	8
2	12
1	24

7b. See page 48l.

7c. As the length increases, the width decreases.

8a. See below right.

8b. See page 48l.

8c. As the length increases, the width decreases.

8d. It would make sense to connect the points because it is possible to use values between the whole numbers for length and width.

9a. See page 48m.

9b. Possible answer: The movie's earnings for the first week suggest that there had been good advertisement to create excitement for the film. The earnings peaked in the second week and then gradually decreased to one million in the eighth week. Approximately $\frac{2}{3}$ of total earnings was made in the first three weeks. Over 80% was earned by the end of the fourth week.

9c. The movie earned a total of 83 million dollars.

9d. See page 48m.

9e. The earnings rose sharply through the second week and then gradually leveled off until the eighth week. In the table, the weekly earnings decrease as the weeks in the theaters increase, so the total earnings increase at a slower rate as the weeks progress. On the graph, the curved line shows the rate of increase lessening each week. This makes sense because many people who were excited about the movie probably saw it in the opening weeks.

8. Recall that the perimeter of a rectangle is the sum of its side lengths.

  a. Make a table of all the possible whole-number values for the length and width of a rectangle with a perimeter of 24 meters.

  b. Make a coordinate graph of your data from part a. Put length on the *x*-axis and width on the *y*-axis.

  c. Describe what happens to the width as the length increases.

  d. Would it make sense to connect the points in this graph? Explain your reasoning.

9. Here are the box office earnings (in millions of dollars) for a popular movie after each of the first eight weeks following its release.

Weeks in theaters	1	2	3	4	5	6	7	8
Weekly earnings (millions of $)	16	22	18	12	7	4	3	1

  a. Make a coordinate graph showing the weekly earnings after each week. Since a film's weekly earnings depend on the number of weeks it is in theaters, put the weeks in theaters on the *x*-axis and the weekly earnings on the *y*-axis.

  b. Write a short description of the pattern of change in the data table and in your graph. Explain how the movie's weekly earnings changed as time passed, how this change is shown in the table and the graph, and why this change might have occured.

  c. What were the *total earnings* of the movie in the eight weeks?

  d. Make a coordinate graph showing the total earnings after each of the first eight weeks.

  e. Write a short description of the pattern of change in your graph of total earnings. Explain how the movie's total earnings changed over time, how this change is shown in the table and the graph, and why this change might have occurred.

8a.

Width (meters)	Length (meters)
1	11
2	10
3	9
4	8
5	7
6	6
7	5
8	4
9	3
10	2
11	1

Extensions

10. You can use *Turtle Math* software to draw regular polygons. At each vertex of a polygon, the turtle must make a turn. The size of the turn is related to the number of sides in the polygon. To draw an equilateral triangle, for example, you have to make 120° turns at each vertex.

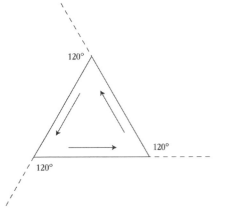

a. Copy and complete the following table, which shows how a turtle turn is related to the number of sides in a regular polygon.

Number of sides	3	4	5	6	7	8	9	10
Degrees in turn	120°							

b. Make a coordinate graph of the (sides, degrees) data.

c. What pattern of change do you see in the degrees the turtle must turn as the number of sides increases? How is that pattern shown in the table? In the graph?

Extensions

10a. See below left.

10b. See page 48m.

10c. As the number of sides increases, the degrees in the turn decrease. In the table, the numbers get smaller. In the graph, the points are placed from the upper left to the lower right (as the graph is read from left to right).

10a.

Number of sides	3	4	5	6	7	8	9	10
Degrees in turn	120°	90°	72°	60°	51.4°	45°	40°	36°

Possible Answers

1. In a table, as the value of *x* increases, the corresponding value of *y* also increases. This is also true in a graph and is shown by a series of points that progress from the lower left of the graph to the upper right.

2. In a table, as the value of *x* increases, the corresponding value of *y* decreases. This is also true on a graph and is shown by a series of points that progress from the upper left of the graph to the lower right.

3. The situations that create linear graphs involve a constant rate of increase or decrease. Students will probably not use this language. They may say that for every change of one unit in the *x* variable, the *y* variable will change by a fixed amount.

4. This question will be revisited throughout the rest of this unit. It asks students to start to think about whether the value between the points on a graph make sense. For example, when talking about time on the *x*-axis, it usually does make sense to connect them since we can think about values between our intervals. When talking about the number of bikes, it would not make sense to connect the points since we do not think about a fractional number of bikes.

Mathematical Reflections

In this investigation, you learned to use data presented in tables and graphs to help you describe patterns of change in two related variables. You used patterns of change to describe how to predict the value of one variable from the value of the other variable. These questions will help you summarize what you have learned:

1 Imagine a situation in which variable *y* depends on variable *x* (for example, *y* might be profit and *x* the number of items sold). If *y* increases as *x* increases, how would this be indicated in a table? In a graph?

2 If variable *y* decreases as variable *x* increases (for example, *y* might be the amount of money in your wallet on a trip and *x* the time you have been traveling), how would this be indicated in a table? In a graph?

3 In a coordinate graph of two related variables, when do the points lie in a straight line?

4 In a coordinate graph of two related variables, when is it appropriate to connect the points?

Think about your answers to these questions, discuss your ideas with other students and your teacher, and then write a summary of your findings in your journal.

48 Variables and Patterns

Tips for the Linguistically Diverse Classroom

Diagram Code The Diagram Code technique is described in detail in *Getting to Know Connected Mathematics*. Students use a minimal number of words and drawings, diagrams, or symbols to respond to questions that require writing. Example: Question 4—A student might respond by drawing a clock (to represent time) under points connected to the word *Yes* underneath, and a picture of bikes under dots not connected to the word *Yes* underneath. To explain their answer, a student might write *10:00* and *11:00* in bold print, with *10:30* between them under the clock picture. Under the bikes, the student might draw two bikes with a half of a bike between them, with a large *X* over the half bike.

3.1 • Renting Bicycles

The introduction expands the conversation about the bicycle tour from time, distance, and speed to money issues. In the problem, students work with a table presentation of one data set and a graphical representation of a different data set. This problem makes the point that data sets presented in different forms are hard to compare. To make comparisons easier, students need to change the form of representation for one of the data sets. Graphing the data from Rocky's Cycle Center table and Adrian's Bike Shop's graph on the same grid or creating a table from the data on Adrian's Bike Shop's graph will allow students to make easier comparisons between the two data sets.

Launch

Read the introduction to the investigation with your students and discuss the questions in the "Think about this!" Make sure students understand the questions being asked, especially words such as *income* (the amount of money taken in from the customers) and *profit* (the amount of money left after all the bills have been paid). Encourage students to share their ideas about what should be provided and to estimate cost for each identified item. Students should give the reasons they believe certain items should be provided by the tour company. They should consider that each additional item costs money and therefore increases the cost of the trip for the customer. Students should challenge each other's estimated costs if they seem unreasonable.

If your students have limited experiences with the context of the problem, you may wish to bring in brochures of various types of bike tours (check cycle or travel magazines) to let students get a feel for the prices of tours.

After summarizing the "Think about this!" conversation, read with your class the introduction to the problem. You may wish to ask these questions to be sure that students understand how to read the table and graph. Then read the problem with the class.

> At Rocky's Cycle Center, what is the cost to rent 5 bicycles? *($400)* 25 bicycles? *($875)* 50 bicycles? *($1200)*
>
> At Adrian's Bike Shop, what is the cost to rent 5 bicycles? *(Estimates will vary. Students will probably estimate between $175 to $185. It is actually $180, but it is not important to find an exact answer at this time.)* 25 bicycles? *(about $780)* 50 bicycles? *(about $1580)*

Explore

Have students work on the problem individually and then in pairs. Some students may need help to recognize that the number of bikes required is an important part of the decision. To help them notice the difference in price, prompt them by asking which bike shop they would choose if they need bikes for ten people, for all the students in our math class, or for four classes the size of ours. This should help them notice the difference in prices between the two companies. Have students who finish early work on the follow-up questions.

Summarize

Have students share their findings regarding which bike shop the tour partners should use and their methods for reaching their conclusions. Ask students:

> What are the two variables in this problem? *(the number of bikes and the rental fee)*
>
> How does the rental fee change as the number of bikes rented increases? *(The total rental fee increases for every additional bike rented.)*
>
> How can you decide which bike shop to choose? *(This depends on the number of bikes you need to rent. Once you determine about how many bikes you will need to rent, compare the cost of both shops for the rentals, and select the shop with the lowest cost.)*

Students should talk about the number of bikes required for the tour. For 35 or fewer bikes, the best value is at Adrian's Bike Shop; for more than 35 bikes, Rocky's Cycle Center has the best value.

> Why was it difficult to compare the prices of the two companies?

Most students will say it is hard to compare the two companies because their data are given in different forms so the differences aren't easy to see. Some students will say that it was hard because the cost for the bikes in the table was given only in multiples of five.

> How did you use the information in the table and the graph to help you decide from which company to rent?

Some students will say they made a table out of the information in the graph because it helped them see how the two companies' prices compared. Because of their prior experiences, some students will suggest graphing the table of data onto the given graph for the other company. If no one suggests representing one of the data sets in a different form, make this suggestion. Both making a table for Adrian's Bike Shop and graphing the data for Rocky's Cycle Center should be explored. The graph of Rocky's Cycle Center should be done on the same graph as Adrian's Bike Shop with a different color so that the two data sets are easy to distinguish.

Continue the conversation by discussing the follow-up questions. Question 1 is very subtle. Some students may suggest that the points be connected because there are data entries between the points. Make sure that students understand that these points should not be connected because one can only rent whole bikes. The *x*-axis could be rescaled to intervals of 1. With this scaling, it is clearer why the points should not be connected.

With follow-up question 2, ask students to explain how they arrived at their rental amount for 32 bikes at each company. After a student has given a method, ask the class if the amount seems reasonable and to explain why. Continue this conversation until all different rental amounts and methods for determining rental fees are presented.

Question 3 of the follow-up asks students to describe in words the pattern of change in the bicycle rentals while question 4 uses these patterns to predict values. Help students see that Adrian's Bike Shop's pattern is regular and easy to describe. Have them notice how the data look on the graph.

How would you describe the arrangements of the points? *(They all lie on a straight line.)*

Would it be difficult to predict beyond the given data with a pattern of this sort? *(No, because the rate of increase is steady.)*

Students may find it more difficult to describe the pattern of change for Rocky's Cycle Center because it does not have the same amount of increase each time. If students cannot describe this, have them graph the data and notice how their data look on the graph. Then have them describe the arrangement of the points on the graph. (They lie on a curve.) Discuss whether it is easier or harder to predict beyond the data in this graph. (It is harder, because the rate of increase is not steady.)

3.2 • Finding Customers

This problem has students graphing data from a table, but this time they must determine which variable goes on which axis and what scale makes sense. After graphing, they are to analyze the data using the graph and/or the table and make a decision about what should be the tour price.

Launch

Read through the problem with your students. They have not been asked to think about why a certain variable is on the *x*-axis since Investigation 1. Leave them to figure this out for themselves. If students chose number of customers instead of price, let them work with this. You can then discuss how easy or difficult it was to make sense of the data with that representation.

We want students to begin thinking about how the price of the tour will affect the number of customers. This problem asks students to think about how they might attract customers and to focus on market research data.

Explore

Encourage students to work individually and complete their own graph. When they are done, it works well to pair the students and have them discuss their graphs, address the rest of the problem, and discuss the follow-up questions. Students may want to redo their graph after talking with their partner. As you walk around to the different groups, encourage students to describe exactly what happens to the number of customers as the price increases by $100, $200, and so on.

Summarize

Have students share graphs, telling what variable they put on which axis and what they chose for a scale for each of the axes. If one student puts the variables on the opposite axes from everyone else, discuss the disadvantages of putting the number of customers on the *x*-axis. (Reversing the variables tells a different story with the shape of the graph. The data represented are exactly the same, but the graph seems to imply that the cost of the tour depends on the number of people rather than the fact that the number of people depends on the price.) Ask students the questions on the following page.

How would you describe the shape of the graph? *(The graph is a curve, decreasing from left to right.)*

How many people would say yes if the price were $100? *(probably between 75 and 80 people)*

Have students share what price should be charged. Collect all students' responses and then discuss their reasons for selecting a certain price. Some students may change their choice after listening to another student's reasons. Ask how much money would be collected in each case if the people who said they would go for a certain price actually do so. Elicit from your students why these results are important and interesting (assuming they are one of the partners for the tour company).

Discuss the follow-up questions, focusing on question 2. Make sure students understand how changes show up in a table and in a graph.

3.3 • Predicting Profit

In this problem, students read from a graph and use points on the graph to predict the location of additional points. They are also asked to informally make sense of the slope of a linear relationship and describe the relationship in words.

Launch

Read through the introduction and the problem with your students. Be sure students understand the relationship the graph represents by asking them what the graph is about. (Sidney is predicting the amount of profit based on the number of tour customers.) Some students may be confused about why the profit is not $350 per customer. If your students struggle with this idea, you will need to discuss the idea that profit is the amount of money left over after the company pays its expenses.

Explore

This is a good problem to work on in pairs because of the size of the problem and the new ideas embedded in the questions. The problem is not extensive, but the new ideas are difficult enough that having another person to think with is helpful. Students may struggle with part D. Help them by asking what happens to business profits when expenses are reduced. Suggest that they increase the profit for each of the x values on the given graph to see what happens. (Profits increase.)

Summarize

Have students share their answers to parts A and B by explaining how they found their answers. Some students may have estimated where the points fall on the profit axis (y-axis) or the number of customers axis (x-axis). Other students may talk about the profit increasing at a steady rate. Since it appears that the points fall in a straight line, they may have found a point that was easy to read, such as $300 profit for 20 customers, and determined that the profit generated by each customer is $15. From this information all the values for the profit are found by multiplying the number of customers by $15, and the number of customers that produce a certain profit is found by dividing the desired profit by $15.

For part C, students should notice that as the number of customers increases, so does the profit. They should also notice that the points fall in a straight line. This tells them that the change between data points is the same. You may wish to introduce the word *linear* to the conversation. (Linear means "in a straight line." Any data that produce a straight-line graph is called a *linear function*, or a *linear relationship*.)

Part D may be difficult for some students. To help them see what would happen, you could create a new data set that has a profit per person of $20 as opposed to the current $15 profit.

Given	New (made up)
10 people, profit–$150	10 people, profit–$200
20 people, profit–$300	20 people, profit–$400
30 people, profit–$450	30 people, profit–$600 (note consistent change)

By graphing the new data set on the same graph as the given data, students should see that more profit makes the line "steeper" (a word commonly used by middle school students at this point in the curriculum).

The follow-up is asking students to begin to look for and describe consistent patterns. Students having difficulty determining the pattern from the graph may benefit from making a table of the data, finding the pattern, and verifying the pattern on the graph.

Number of customers	Profit ($)
1	15
2	30
3	45
100	1500

If you ask students to describe the pattern of change in the table, they should be able to tell you that for each additional customer the profit goes up $15. Write what they say in words on the board. Describing a predictable pattern in words starts the process of learning to describe a predictable pattern in symbols involving algebraic rules.

3.4 • Paying Bills and Counting Profits

This problem is an introduction to searching for rules from which to calculate other amounts or, in other words, describing consistent patterns. At this point, we want students to look for patterns and see relationships between two variables, such as number of customers and income, and then describe these patterns in words.

Launch

Rewriting the pattern from words to symbols can be discussed with students. However, do not expect students to be able to write algebraic rules for consistent patterns easily. We just want to introduce the ideas. Investigation 4 has students working with letters representing variables, and we come back to this idea in the future algebra units.

Read through the problem with your students, emphasizing that the tour company only rents one van for each trip. The number of vans needed does not change.

Explore

Have students make their own table first. Then, combine them in groups of two or three to work on the other parts to the problem. Ask them to look for patterns and to describe the ones they find. These questions give students another opportunity to deal with linear situations. Students might not recognize these as linear because the information is in a table instead of a graph.

For students having difficulty, have them talk about the entries in their tables with their partners. Sharing ways to compute new values and putting these ideas into words will help all the students in a group.

For the Teacher: Saving Data for Problem 4.3

Students revisit this situation in Problem 4.3. Have them keep a record of their data from part B for reference when using symbols to write rules.

Summarize

Display Transparency 3.4B, Sidney's table, showing only the information that is given in the student edition. Ask a student to fill in the first column on income. After the additional information has been recorded, ask students how they found the amounts for the income column. Write their explanation in words. This is an important step in learning how to use symbols to write rules and understanding the symbolic language of mathematics. You may wish to write a short version of students' rules, underlining words that translate into symbols. For example, suppose students tell you that *to find the amounts for the income column, you multiply the number of customers you have by $350.* Then ask students, "If I wanted to say this same thing using fewer words, does it make sense for me to write *amount of income = # of customers × $350?*"

Continue this same line of questioning and student participation as you look at the bike rental costs and the food and camp costs. Even though descriptive patterns are not asked for in the problem, talking about them will help students to find and describe patterns.

Filling in the total cost column and observing that it increases by $155 with each new customer is more difficult than completing the other columns. Several students will likely be able to describe the pattern of change but have difficulty describing how to find the total cost for any number of customers. With some guiding questions, students can see that the cost is $155 times the number of customers plus $700.

Finding profit in part D will be possible for most students even though the problem deals with being in debt and negative numbers. Students will probably be able to find the amounts, even the negative amounts, but not be able to verbalize how they got these amounts or demonstrate any true understanding of what it means to operate with negative numbers. Don't worry about this now. Students will come back to these ideas in *Accentuate the Negative,* a unit on integers.

Discuss the follow-up questions. Have students think about what is a reasonable amount of pay for a summer job as they justify their answer for question 3.

Additional Answers

Answers to Problem 3.1 Follow-Up

2. The cost of renting 32 bikes from Rocky's Cycle Center is about $1013. (The difference between renting 30 bikes and 35 bikes is $95. Divided among the five additional bikes makes it $19 each for every additional bike after 30. ($975 + $19 + $19 = $1013) Since Adrian's Bike Shop rents bikes at the rate of $30 each, the cost of renting 32 bikes will be $960. (32 × $30 = $960)

3. Answers will vary. Adrian's Bike Shop rents 20 bikes for $600 and appears to rent at a constant rate, charging $30 for each bike rented. Rocky's Cycle Center charges a lot for the first five bikes but, with each additional five bikes, the additional charge decreases.

4. Answers will vary. It is easy to predict the cost for bikes from Adrian's Bike Shop. Since each bike costs $30, any answer will be a multiple of 30. One way to predict the cost for renting from Rocky's Cycle Center is to first find the two "Number of bikes" rentals in the table between which the number of bikes they wish to rent falls. Then, subtract the two rental fees and divide by 5 to get the price per bike for this interval; add this price for each bike rental made in that interval to the rental fee for the lower of the two "Number of bikes" rentals. If the number of bikes needed to rent is greater than the number in the table, the student may assume that it will be $24 for each additional bike (the cost per bike for 50). Another reasonable argument would have the cost per bike declining as the number of bikes increases, since that is the pattern in the table.

Answers to Problem 3.2

B.

Tour Price Projections

C. Answers will vary. Based on the graph, we should charge around $250 because after that the number of customers falls off faster.

To help students better understand what is happening, encourage them to also make a table like the one shown on the next page, which shows the amount of income for each number of customers. If we multiply the number of customers by the price of the tour, we find the amount of income.

Price	Number of customers	Income (price × number of customers)
$150	76	$11,400
200	74	14,800
250	71	17,750
300	65	19,500
350	59	20,650
400	49	19,600
450	38	17,100
500	26	13,000
550	14	7700
600	0	0

Most students will then choose $350 because the most income would be earned at this price. Encourage them to think of other real-world considerations that might influence them to choose a different price. For example, the tour might be more successful in the long run if the number of customers was small at first, since people will not want to go on a crowded tour. Hence, the tour operators should charge $500. On the other hand, people will expect more if they pay more, so they might have more dissatisfied customers if they charge $350 instead of $200. With $200 as the price, they might have more repeat customers and better public relations, which could mean more profit in the long run.

Answers to Problem 3.2 Follow-Up

2. In the table, the number of potential customers decreases as you move down. In the graph, the number of customers falls from 76 to 0 as you move from left to right on the x-axis.

Answer to Problem 3.3 Follow-Up

The profit for 1 customer is $15, for 2 customers is $30, for 3 customers is $45, and for 100 customers is $150. For any number of customers, the amount of profit is 15 times the number of customers. (Note: At this time, we are not going for the rule $P = 15n$. Letters as variables will be introduced in the next investigation.)

Answers to Problem 3.4

A. The table has been extended to show "Total cost" and "Profit," which are not referred to until parts C and D.

Number of customers	Income	Bike rental	Food and camp costs	Van rental	Total cost	Profit
1	$350	$30	$125	$700	$855	−$505
2	700	60	250	700	1010	−310
3	1050	90	375	700	1165	−115
4	1400	120	500	700	1320	80
5	1750	150	625	700	1475	275
6	2100	180	750	700	1630	470
7	2450	210	875	700	1785	665
8	2800	240	1000	700	1940	860
9	3150	270	1125	700	2095	1055
10	3500	300	1250	700	2250	1250

D. 5 riders would yield a profit of $275: $(5 \times 350) - (5 \times 155 + 700) = \$275$
10 riders would yield a profit of $1250: $(10 \times 350) - (10 \times 155 + 700) = \$1250$
25 riders would yield a profit of $4175: $(25 \times 350) - (25 \times 155 + 700) = \$4175$

Answers to Problem 3.4 Follow-Up

1. Possible answer: The bike rental cost increases by $30 with each new person added to the tour. The food and camp costs increase by $125 with each new person added to the tour. The profit increases more rapidly than total cost.

2. Four customers, which gives a profit of $80.

3. Possible answer: Around 20 customers since this gives the tour company a profit of $3200, which must be divided five ways with each individual making $640. Since the tour directors also need food and a place to camp, $125 would need to be deducted from each individual's profit. The result would be a profit of $515 per person, which is a fair return for one week's work.

ACE Answers

Applications

1a.

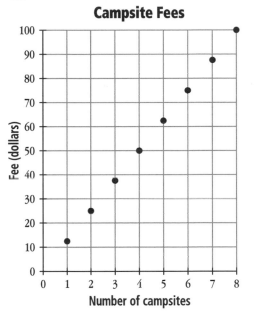

2a. Though it does not make sense to talk about a fractional part of a camper, the points on the graph have been connected to make the pattern clearer.

Supply Rental

Number of campers	Gear rental fee ($)
0	0
5	125
10	250
15	375
20	500
25	625
30	750
35	875
40	1000
45	1125
50	1250

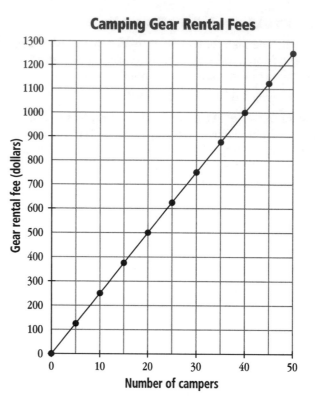

Camping Gear Rental Fees

3a. The fees in the table are rounded to the nearest dollar.

Distance (miles)	Fee ($)
0	0
25	106
50	213
75	319
100	425
125	531
150	638
175	744
200	850
225	956
250	1063
275	1169
300	1275

3b. The fees in the table are rounded to the nearest dollar.

Distance (miles)	Fee ($)
0	200
25	250
50	300
75	350
100	400
125	450
150	500
175	550
200	600
225	650
250	700
275	750
300	800

3c. Appearance of graphs may vary because scales may differ.

Truck Rental Cost

(y-axis: Rental charge (dollars), x-axis: Distance (miles))

Legend:
● East Coast Trucks
△ Philadelphia Truck Rental

4a. To answer this question, students might graph the data for Source Video or make a table for Extreme Video. If Dezi rents 2 movies each month, he would rent 24 movies each year. The cost of 24 movies would be $54 at Source Video and $60 at Extreme Video. So, Source Video is a better choice for Dezi's family. These can be found on either the table or graph.

Video Rentals

(y-axis: Rental cost (dollars), x-axis: Number of videos)

Legend:
- - - Source Video
—— Extreme Video

Number of videos	0	5	10	15	20	25	30
Extreme Video ($)	0	12.50	25.00	37.50	50.00	62.50	75.00
Source Video ($)	30.00	35.00	40.00	45.00	50.00	55.00	60.00

Connections

7b. Appearance of graphs may vary because scales may differ. Although the problem asks students only about rectangles with whole-number side lengths, the points on the graph have been connected to make the pattern clearer.

Rectangle with Area of 24 Square Meters

8b. Appearance of graphs may vary because scales may differ.

Rectangles with Perimeter of 24 Meters

9a. Possible graph:

Box Office Earnings

9d. Possible graph:

Total Box Office Earnings

Extensions

10b. Appearance of graphs may vary because scales may differ.

Regular Polygons

Patterns and Rules

Most situations in the remainder of this unit are linear. In a linear relationship, there is a constant rate of change between the variables—that is, for each unit change in one variable there is a constant change in the second variable. Hence, the graph is a straight line. Formal work on the differences between linear and nonlinear situations will come in later units—grade 7 unit *Moving Straight Ahead* and grade 8 units *Growing, Growing, Growing; Frogs, Fleas, and Painted Cubes;* and *Say It with Symbols.*

In this investigation, students study tables and graphs of linear situations involving distance, rate, and time to see if they can find a pattern that relates the variables. They are asked to describe the relationship in their own words and then with symbols. In Problem 4.1, Heading Home, students create and interpret a table, graph, and a rule for the situation described by $d = 55t$. In Problem 4.2, Changing Speeds, students explore what happens at different speeds by looking at $d = 50t$ and $d = 65t$. Problem 4.3, Calculating Costs and Profits, asks students to revisit Problem 3.4 and write symbolic rules for cost and profit.

Mathematical and Problem-Solving Goals

- *To understand the relationship between rate, time, and distance*

- *To represent information regarding rates in tables and graphs and to use tables and graphs to compare rates*

- *To search for patterns of predictable change*

- *To learn to express in words and symbols situations that change in predictable ways*

Materials		
Problem	**For students**	**For the teacher**
All	Graphing calculators, grid paper (provided as a blackline master)	Transparencies 4.1A to 4.3B (optional)

Student Pages 49–60   Teaching the Investigation 60a–60i

Patterns and Rules

So far in this unit, you have studied many of the variables involved in the Ocean and History Bike Tours business. By using tables and graphs, you have investigated how these variables are related to one another. For example, you explored how the number of customers is related to profit and how the number of hours of riding is related to the distance covered. As you study how variables are related, you are learning about algebra.

Sometimes the relationship between two variables can be described with a simple **rule**. Such rules are very helpful in making predictions for values that are not included in a table or a graph of a set of data. In previous investigations, you described rules in words. In this investigation, you will use symbols to express rules. Here are some examples:

- If the tour operators charge $350 per customer, the rule for calculating the tour income can be expressed as:

$$\text{income} = 350 \times \text{number of customers}$$

  This rule gives the relationship between income and the number of customers: the income is 350 times the number of customers.

- The rule for calculating the circumference of a bicycle wheel (or any circle) can be written as:

  $$\text{circumference} = \pi \times \text{diameter}$$

  You can use this rule to calculate the circumference of any circle, as long as you know its diameter.

Rules, like those above, that are expressed with mathematical symbols are sometimes referred to as **equations** or **formulas**.

Investigation 4: Patterns and Rules 49

Launch

- Introduce the use of rules written in both words and symbols to show the relationship between two variables.

- Discuss the relationship between rate, time, and distance.

Explore

- As groups of two or three work, suggest that students having difficulty using fractions draw pictures to help make sense of the problem.

Summarize

- Encourage groups to explain their answers and why they are reasonable.

- Have students compare their rules written in words with the ones written in symbols.

- Emphasize that while the letters used as variables are arbitrary, they must be defined for the equation to make sense.

Assignment Choices

ACE questions 10, 13, and unassigned choices from earlier problems

A shorter way to write rules relating variables is to replace the word names for the variables with single letters. For example, in the rule for income, you could write I for *income* and n for the *number of customers*. The rule would then become:

$$I = 350 \times n$$

If you let C stand for *circumference* and d stand for *diameter*, you could write the rule for the circumference of a wheel as:

$$C = \pi \times d$$

You can shorten these rules even more. In algebra, when a number is multiplied by a variable, the multiplication sign is often omitted. So, you could write the above rules as:

$$I = 350n \qquad \text{and} \qquad C = \pi d$$

When you see a rule, such as $I = 350n$, with a number next to a letter, multiply. So, $I = 350n$ means $I = 350 \times n$ and $C = \pi d$ means $C = \pi \times d$.

 ## Heading Home

When the Ocean and History Bike Tour reached Williamsburg, the tired riders packed their bikes and gear in the van and headed back toward Philadelphia. They traveled by interstate highway, and averaged a steady 55 miles per hour for the 310-mile trip home.

You have seen that making a table and a graph can help you understand how the time and the distance traveled are related.

Time (hours)	Distance (miles)
0	
1	
2	
3	
4	
5	
6	
7	
8	

Answers to Problem 4.1

A. See page 60e.

B. Estimates will vary but should be close to these values:

1. 165 miles   2. 247.5 miles   3. 288.75 miles

C. 1. 550 miles   2. $678\frac{1}{3}$ miles   3. 825 miles

D. To find distance traveled, you multiply time traveled by 55.

E. $d = 55t$

Problem 4.1

A. Copy and complete the table and graph on the previous page to show the relationship between distance and time if the students traveled at a rate of 55 miles per hour.

B. Use your table and graph to estimate the total distance traveled after

   1. 3 hours   **2.** $4\frac{1}{2}$ hours   **3.** $5\frac{1}{4}$ hours

C. If the students continued driving at a steady 55 miles per hour, how far would they go in

   1. 10 hours   **2.** $12\frac{1}{3}$ hours   **3.** 15 hours

D. Look for patterns in the table and graph that help you calculate the distance traveled for any given time. Write a rule, using words, that explains how to calculate the distance traveled for any given time.

E. Use symbols to write your rule from part D as an equation.

▨ Problem 4.1 Follow-Up

1. How could you find the distance traveled after $3\frac{1}{4}$ hours by using the table? The graph? The equation?

2. Estimate how much time it took the students to reach each of the following cities on their route:

   a. Richmond, Virginia—about 55 miles from Williamsburg

   b. Baltimore, Maryland—about $\frac{3}{4}$ of the way from Williamsburg to Philadelphia

   c. Philadelphia, Pennsylvania—about 310 miles from Williamsburg

4.2 Changing Speeds

The speed limit on many sections of the interstate highway is 65 miles per hour. If the students had traveled at this speed for the whole trip, it would have taken them less time to get home. However, if they had stopped for rest and food breaks, they would have probably averaged a slower speed, such as 50 miles per hour.

At a Glance

Grouping: individuals, then pairs

Launch

- Have students predict the differences in travel times for the trip to Philadelphia at various speeds.

- Remind students to graph all data on the same coordinate grid using different colors.

Explore

- Have students make their own tables and graphs and then discuss their work in pairs.

- Have students think about whether the graph or the tables provide a better way to compare these data.

Summarize

- Discuss students' answers to the problem.

- As students share their responses to parts D and E, have them evaluate all answers for reasonableness.

Answers to Problem 4.1 Follow-Up

1. The table gives the distances for 3 and 4 hours. Add one quarter of the difference between these times (13.75) to the distance for 3 hours to find the total distance (165 + 13.75 = 178.75). On the graph, the distance can be found by locating the point one quarter of the way between 3 and 4 on the *x*-axis. Draw an imaginary perpendicular line that intersects the *x*-axis and the graph, and then draw an imaginary perpendicular line from this point of intersection to the *y*-axis. This point shows the distance traveled (about 175 miles). In the equation, substitute $3\frac{1}{4}$ (or 3.25) for the variable *t* ($3.25 \times 55 = 178.75$).

2.   a.   1 h

     b.   about 4 h 15 min

     c.   about 5 h 40 min

Assignment Choices

ACE questions 1, 2, 8, 9, and unassigned choices from earlier problems

4.3

Calculating Costs and Profits

Grouping:
pairs

Launch

- Students will need to use their entries from Problem 3.4 to rewrite rules using symbols.

- Allow students to attack the problem without much preliminary discussion.

Explore

- Have students work in pairs.

- Refer students having difficulty to their work for Problem 3.4. Help them by asking how to represent a word or group of words with a symbol.

Summarize

- Write all solutions on the board.

- Discuss which rules are reasonable and why they are correct.

- Have the class revise incorrect rules, explaining why the changes were made.

Problem 4.2

A. Make tables of time and distance data, similar to the table you made for Problem 4.1, for travel at 50 miles per hour and 65 miles per hour.

Plot the data from both tables on one coordinate grid. Use a different color for each set of data. Using a third color, add data points for the times and distances traveled at 55 miles per hour (from Problem 4.1).

B. How are the tables for the three speeds similar? How are they different?

C. How are the graphs for the three speeds similar? How are they different?

D. 1. Look at the table and graph for 65 miles per hour. What pattern of change in the data helps you calculate the distance for any given time? In words, write a rule that explains how to calculate the distance traveled for any given time.

    2. Use symbols to write your rule as an equation.

E. 1. Now write a rule, in words, that explains how to calculate the distance traveled for any given time when the speed is 50 miles per hour.

    2. Use symbols to write your rule as an equation.

F. How are the rules for calculating distance for the three speeds similar? How are they different?

■ **Problem 4.2 Follow-Up**

1. After arriving in Philadelphia, Malcolm took the interstate home. He wrote the equation $d = 60t$ to represent his trip home. Explain this equation in words.

2. How long would it take to reach Philadelphia—310 miles from Williamsburg—traveling at 50 miles per hour? 60 miles per hour? 65 miles per hour?

4.3 Calculating Costs and Profits

Sidney started a table like the one on the next page to help the partners determine their profit for the tour. In Problem 3.4, you completed this table for up to 10 customers. You also wrote rules, in words, describing the patterns of change you found in the table.

Sidney wants to use symbols to write equations for these rules, so she can predict costs and profit for any number of customers. For example, in the introduction of this unit the equation for the rule for calculating income was given as $I = 350 \times n$, or $I = 350n$, where I represents the income in dollars for n customers.

Assignment Choices

ACE questions 3–7, 11, 12, 14, and unassigned choices from earlier problems

Assessment

It is appropriate to use the quiz after this problem.

Answers to Problem 4.2

See page 60f.

Answers to Problem 4.2 Follow-Up

1. The equation $d = 60t$ means that for each hour traveled at a rate of 60 miles per hour, you will go 60 miles further.

2. At 50 miles per hour, it will take 6.2 hours or about 6 hours 12 minutes to go 310 miles. At 60 miles per hour, it will take 5.17 hours or about 5 hours 10 minutes. At 65 miles per hour, it will take 4.77 hours or about 4 hours 46 minutes.

Number of customers	Income	Bike rental	Food and camp costs	Van rental	Total cost	Profit
1	$350	$30	$125	$700	$855	−$505
2	700	60	250	700	1010	−310
3	1050	90	375	700	1165	−115
4	1400	120	500	700	1320	80
5	1750	150	625	700	1475	275
6	2100	180	750	700	1630	470
7	2450	210	875	700	1785	665
8	2800	240	1000	700	1940	860
9	3150	270	1125	700	2095	1055
10	3500	300	1250	700	2250	1250

Problem 4.3

A. Write an equation for the rule to calculate each of the following costs for any number, n, of customers.

1. bike rental   **2.** food and camp costs   **3.** van rental

B. Write an equation for the rule to determine the *total cost* for any number, n, of customers.

C. Write an equation for the rule to determine the *profit* for any number, n, of customers.

Problem 4.3 Follow-Up

1. Theo's father has a van he will let the students use at no charge. Which of these equations represents the total cost if they use his van?

a. $C = 125 + 30$ **b.** $C = 125n + 30n$
c. $C = 155$ **d.** $C = 155 + n$

2. If the partners require customers to supply their own bikes, which of these is the new equation for total cost? (Assume the students will rent a van.)

a. $C = 125n + 700$ **b.** $C = 125 + 700 + n$
c. $825n$ **d.** $C = 350n + 125n + 700$

3. If customers must supply their own bikes, which equations below represent the profit? (Assume the students will rent a van.)

a. $P = 350 - (125 + 700 + n)$ **b.** $P = 350n - 125n + 700$
c. $P = 350n - (125n + 700)$ **d.** $P = 350n - 125n - 700$

Answers to Problem 4.3

A.   1. $C = 30n$ 2. $C = 125n$ 3. $C = 700$

B. $C = 30n + 125n + 700$ or $C = 155n + 700$

C. $P = 350n - 30n - 125n - 700$ or $P = 350n - 155n - 700$ or $P = 350n - (155n + 700)$ or $P = 195n - 700$

Answers to Problem 4.3 Follow-Up

1. b

2. a

3. c and d

Answers

Applications

1a. See page 60g.

1b. Estimates should be close to the following:

i.   120 mi
ii. 165 mi
iii. 210 mi
iv. 435 mi

1c. The data are represented in the table by corresponding *x* and *y* values equal to 2 and 120, respectively. They are represented by point (2, 120) on the graph.

1d. See below right.

1e. The distance (in miles) is 60 multiplied by time (in hours), or *d* = 60*t*.

1f. $1\frac{1}{2}$ h

1g. about 3 h 7 min

1h. $9\frac{1}{3}$ h, or 9 h 20 min

As you work on these ACE questions, use your calculator whenever you need it.

Applications

1. The El Paso Middle School girls' basketball team drove from El Paso to San Antonio for the Texas State Championship game. The trip was 560 miles. Their bus averaged 60 miles per hour on the trip.

   a. Make a table and a graph of time and distance data for the basketball team's bus.

   b. Estimate the distance traveled by the bus after each of the following times:

   i. 2 hours   **ii.** $2\frac{3}{4}$ hours   **iii.** $3\frac{1}{2}$ hours   **iv.** 7.25 hours

   c. How are 2 hours and the distance traveled in 2 hours represented in the table? On the graph?

   d. How are $2\frac{3}{4}$ hours and the distance traveled in $2\frac{3}{4}$ hours represented in the table? On the graph?

   e. What rule relating time and distance could help you calculate the distance traveled for any given time on this trip?

   f. The bus route passed through Sierra Blanca, Texas, which is 90 miles from El Paso. How long did it take the bus to get to Sierra Blanca?

   g. The bus route also passed through Balmorhea, Texas, which is $\frac{1}{3}$ of the way from El Paso to San Antonio. How long did it take the bus to get to Balmorhea?

   h. How long did it take the bus to complete its 560-mile trip to San Antonio?

1d. Answers will vary depending on the values students used to construct their tables and graphs. If students opted to list the values in their tables by quarters of an hour, they will be able to read the distance covered in $2\frac{3}{4}$ hours by finding the corresponding *y* value for that time. Other students will need to estimate the distance using the corresponding *y* values for the times closest to $2\frac{3}{4}$ hours shown in their tables. If students have used a scale in quarter-hour increments on the *x*-axis on the graph, they can find the distance traveled by drawing a perpendicular line from $2\frac{3}{4}$ on the *x*-axis to the graph. If they have used an alternate scale, they will need to approximate the place on the *x*-axis that shows the point and proceed in the same manner. From this point on the graph, they can draw a straight line that is perpendicular to the *y*-axis. The value of the *y*-coordinate at the intersection of this line with the *y*-axis is the distance traveled.

2. The equation $d = 70t$ represents the distance, in miles, covered after traveling at 70 miles per hour for t hours.

    a. Make a table that shows the distance traveled, according to this equation, for every half hour between 0 hours and 4 hours.

    b. Sketch a graph that shows the distance traveled between 0 and 4 hours.

    c. If $t = 2.5$ hours, what is d?

    d. If $d = 210$ miles, what is t?

    e. You probably made your graph by plotting points. In this situation, would it make sense to connect these points with line segments?

In 3–6, use symbols to express the rule as an equation. Use single letters to stand for the variables. Identify what each letter represents.

3. The area of a rectangle is its length multiplied by its width.

4. The number of hot dogs needed for the picnic is two for each student.

5. Taxi fare is $2.00 plus $1.10 per mile.

6. The amount of material needed to make the curtains is $4\frac{3}{8}$ yards per window.

7. This table shows the relationship between the number of riders on a bike tour and the daily cost of providing box lunches.

Customers	1	2	3	4	5	6	7	8	9
Lunch cost	$4.25	8.50	12.75	17.00	21.25	25.50	29.75	34.00	38.25

    a. Write an equation for a rule relating lunch cost, L, and number of customers, n.

    b. Use your equation to find the lunch cost if 25 people are on the tour.

    c. How many people could eat lunch if the tour leader had $89.25?

2a. See below left.

2b. See page 60h.

2c. $d = 175$ miles

2d. $t = 3$ hours

2e. Yes, in this case the information represented by a line connecting the points is accurate because the distance increases at a constant rate (so there would not be any jumps or curves between points).

3. $A = l \times w$ or $A = lw$ (where A = area, l = length, and w = width)

4. $H = 2 \times s$ or $H = 2s$ (where H = number of hot dogs and s = number of students)

5. $T = 2 + 1.10 \times m$ or $T = 2 + 1.10m$ (where T = taxi fare and m = number of miles)

6. $Y = 4\frac{3}{8} \times w$ or $Y = 4\frac{3}{8}w$ (where Y = number of yards and w = number of windows)

7a. $L = 4.25n$

7b. $L = 4.25 \times 25 = 106.25

7c. If $89.25 = 4.25n$, what number multiplied by 4.25 gives 89.25? $n = 21$ people

2a.

Time (hours)	0	0.5	1.0	1.5	2.0	2.5	3.0	3.5	4.0
Distance (miles)	0	35	70	105	140	175	210	245	280

Connections

8a. Kai will travel 84.78 inches in one turn because the circumference of his wheel is 3.14 × 27 inches, or 84.78 inches.

8b. Masako will travel 62.80 inches for one turn because the circumference of her wheel is 3.14 × 20 inches, or 62.80 inches.

8c. Kai will travel 42,390 inches for 500 turns because 84.78 × 500 = 42,390. Students may choose to convert this to 3532.5 feet or 1177.5 yards.

8d. Masako will travel 31,400 inches for 500 turns because 62.80 × 500 = 31,400. Students may choose to convert this to 2617 feet or 872 yards.

Connections

In 8 and 9, use the following information: In previous units, you discovered that the circumference, radius, and diameter of a circle are related. These relationships involve a special number named with the Greek letter π. The exact value of π is an infinite decimal that begins 3.14159265358. The approximation 3.14 is commonly used. For any circle:

$$\text{circumference} = \pi \times \text{diameter}$$

Since the diameter of a circle is twice its radius, you can also write this as:

$$\text{circumference} = \pi \times 2 \times \text{radius}$$

8. The wheels on Kai's bike are 27 inches in diameter. His little sister, Masako, has a bike with wheels that are 20 inches in diameter. Sometimes Kai and Masako go out for evening bike rides around their neighborhood.

a. How far will Kai go in one complete turn of his wheels?

b. How far will Masako go in one complete turn of her wheels?

c. How far will Kai go in 500 turns of his wheels?

d. How far will Masako go in 500 turns of her wheels?

e. How many times will Kai's wheels have to turn to cover 100 feet? (Remember that there are 12 inches in 1 foot.)

f. How many times will Masako's wheels have to turn to cover 100 feet?

g. How many times will Kai's wheels have to turn to cover 1 mile? (Remember that there are 5280 feet in 1 mile.)

h. How many times will Masako's wheels have to turn in order to cover 1 mile?

9. The old-fashioned bicycle shown here is called a "penny farthing" bicycle. These bikes had front wheels as large as 5 feet in diameter! Suppose the front wheel of this bicycle has a diameter of 5 feet.

a. What is the radius of the front wheel?

b. How far will this bike travel in 100 turns of the front wheel?

c. How many times will the front wheel turn in a 3-mile trip?

d. Compare the number of times the wheels of Masako's bike turn in a 1-mile trip (see question 8h) with the number of times the front wheel of this penny farthing bike turns in a 3-mile trip. Why do the numbers compare this way?

10. Celia came up with the equation $d = 8t$ to represent the number of miles the bikers could travel in t hours at a speed of 8 miles per hour.

a. Make a table that shows the distance traveled every half hour, up to 5 hours, if the bikers ride at this constant speed for 5 hours.

b. How far would the bikers travel in 1 hour? 3 hours?

8g. about 747 turns; Students' methods of computation will vary. If students convert miles to inches (5280 feet = 63,360 inches), Kai's wheels will make $\frac{63,360}{84.78} \approx 747.35$. If students answer using the number of turns, Kai's wheels make approximately 14.15 turns every 100 feet. Since there are 52.8 hundreds in 5280 feet, $14.15 \times 52.8 = 747.12$ turns.

8h. about 1009 turns; Students' methods of computation will vary. If students convert miles to inches, Masako's wheels will make $\frac{63,360}{62.80} \approx 1008.92$ turns. If students answer using the number of turns, Masako's wheels make approximately 19.1 turns every 100 feet. Since there are 52.8 hundreds in 5280 feet, $19.1 \times 52.8 = 1008.48$ turns.

10a.

Time (hours)	0	0.5	1.0	1.5	2.0	2.5	3.0	3.5	4.0	4.5	5.0
Distance (miles)	0	4	8	12	16	20	24	28	32	36	40

8e. Kai's wheels will make $\frac{1200}{84.78}$ = about 14.15 turns.

8f. Masako's wheels will make $\frac{1200}{62.80}$ = about 19.11 turns.

8g. See below left.

8h. See below left.

9a. 2.5 feet

9b. The bike will travel $3.14 \times 5 = 15.7$ feet in one turn, so in 100 turns it will travel 1570 feet.

9c. Since 3 miles = 15,840 feet, it will make $\frac{15,840}{15.7} =$ about 1008.9 turns.

9d. The big wheel can go three times as far for the same number of turns because its diameter is three times the diameter of Masako's wheel (20 in. = $1\frac{2}{3}$ ft compared with 5 ft).

10a. See below left.

10b. 8 miles in 1 hour, 24 miles in 3 hours, 36 miles in 4.5 hours, 48 miles in 6 hours. (The first three values can be read from the table. For 6 hours, students will need to use the equation $d = 8(6) = 48$ miles.)

11a. $290 after 1 payment; $265 after 2 payments; $240 after 3 payments

11b. $A = 315 - 25n$

11c. See page 60h.

11d. As number of weeks increases by 1, the amount still owed decreases by $25. As we read down the "Number of weeks" column in the table and look at the corresponding amount owed, we see that the amount decreases by $25 for each increase of one week. In the graph this is shown by the line sloped downward as we read from left to right. More specifically, if we move 1 unit to the right on the x-axis, the line moves downward a corresponding $25 on the y-axis.

11e. Sean will pay off the loan after 13 weeks; he will have only a $15 payment the last week. This is shown in the table by the amount owed going below 0 at 13 weeks, and in the graph we see that the line goes below the x-axis for the first time during the thirteenth week, indicating that that is the week when Sean no longer owes any money.

Extensions

12a. See table at right. Speeds are rounded to the nearest tenth.

12b. $s = \frac{d}{t}$

---

11. Sean just bought a new CD player and speakers from the Audio Source for $315. The store offered Sean an interest-free payment plan that allows him to pay in weekly installments of $25.

 a. How much will Sean still owe after one payment? After two payments? After three payments?

 b. Using n to stand for the number of payments and A for the amount still owed, write an equation for calculating A for any given value of n.

 c. Use your equation to make a table and a graph showing the relationship between n and A.

 d. As n increases by 1, how does A change? How is this change shown in the table? On the graph?

 e. How many payments will Sean have to make in all? How is this shown in the table? How is this shown on the graph?

Extensions

12. a. If you know the distance and the time you have traveled on a car trip, you can calculate the average speed of the trip. Find the average speed for each pair of distance and time values below.

Distance (miles)	Time (hours)	Average speed (miles per hour)
145	2	_____
110	2	_____
165	2.5	_____
300	5.25	_____
446	6.75	_____
528	8	_____
862	9.5	_____
723	10	_____

 b. Write an equation for calculating the average speed, s, for any distance, d, and time, t.

12a.

Distance (miles)	Time (hours)	Average speed (miles per hour)
145	2	72.5
110	2	55.0
165	2.5	66.0
300	5.25	57.1
446	6.75	66.1
528	8	66.0
862	9.5	90.7
723	10	72.3

13. The trip from Ocean City, Maryland, to Chincoteague Island, Virginia, is about 40 miles.

    a. How long will the trip take if the riders average 6 miles per hour?

    b. How would the time for the trip change if the average speed increased? If the average speed decreased?

14. Maurice and Cheri made graphs of the equation $y = 4x + 20$ in their math class.

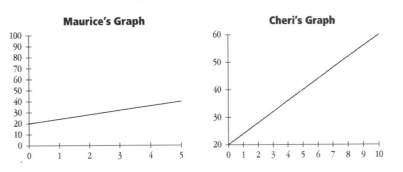

    a. Describe the similarities between the two graphs.

    b. Describe the differences between the two graphs.

    c. Can both of these graphs represent the same equation? Explain your reasoning.

13a. 40 ÷ 6 = about 6.7 hours

13b. See page 60i.

14a. Possible answer: They have the same points. For example, points (0, 20), (1, 24), (2, 28), (3, 32), (4, 36), and (5, 40) are on both graphs. Both graphs show an increase.

14b. Possible answer: The graphs have a different steepness—Cheri's seems to be steeper. They also have different scales.

14c. The graphs do represent the same equation. The difference in appearance is due to the difference in scale used on each axis.

1. $d = 60t$

2. Students might have other ideas, but be sure they understand at least these basic concepts: Using the rule, we can calculate d or t from *any* given value of the other variable. A graph gives us a quick visual image, while a table gives us quick information (no calculations required) for a limited range of values of d and t.

Mathematical Reflections

In this investigation, you learned to use symbols to write equations for rules relating variables. These questions will help you summarize what you have learned:

1 The Larson family is traveling from Michigan to Florida at an average speed of 60 miles per hour. Write an equation for a rule you can you use to calculate the distance they have traveled after any given number of hours.

2 What are the advantages of having an equation to represent the Larson family's situation? What are the advantages to having a table? A graph?

Think about your answers to these questions, discuss your ideas with other students and your teacher, and then write a summary of your findings in your journal.

Tips for the Linguistically Diverse Classroom

Original Rebus The Original Rebus technique is described in detail in *Getting to Know Connected Mathematics*. Students make a copy of the text before it is discussed. During the discussion, they generate their own rebuses for words they do not understand; the words are made comprehensible through pictures, objects, or demonstrations. Example: Question 1—key words for which students may make rebuses are *Larson family* (stick figures representing people of various ages), *traveling* (a car), *Michigan and Florida* (outlines of the states), *equation* (triangle = square), *calculate the distance* (a line drawn between the outlines of the two states).

4.1 • Heading Home

This problem has students look at variables that have a linear relationship. Students are asked to create a table, a graph, and write the relationship between the variables in both words and symbols. The purpose of this problem is to help students learn how to construct rules for predictable patterns and to recognize these patterns in tables, graphs, and rules. The problem also explores the relationship between these different representations.

Launch

Read through the introduction of the investigation with your students. The text introduces students to writing rules in symbolic form. Once they understand this, move on to Problem 4.1.

Read through the introduction and the problem with your students. Discuss the relationship between rate, time, and distance. Ask students what common rates, such as 55 miles per hour, mean. Then ask how long it will take someone going 55 miles per hour to travel a distance of 55 miles, 110 miles, and 220 miles (1 hour, 2 hours, and 4 hours). By now, creating tables and graphs should be easy for your students. This problem asks them to use these two representations and what they understand about the relationship between time and distance to answer some questions.

Explore

Have students work in groups of two or three. Encourage groups to plan to be able to explain how they found each answer and why each is reasonable. Students having difficulty using fractions may wish to seek help from each other. You might also suggest that they draw pictures to help them make sense of what the problem is asking.

Summarize

Ask students to share their answers to part B. Record students' answers to questions 1, 2, and 3 on the board. When all solutions are recorded, have students explain how they found their solutions and why their answers are reasonable. The time $5\frac{1}{4}$ hours is most likely to produce different solutions. Repeat the procedure for part C.

The students' explanations for part C should move the discussion to the relationship between time and distance as a rule. Have students record the rules from part D on the board. Use these descriptions to have students explain how they can replace the words with symbols as requested in part E. Discuss how the two different-looking rules state the same thing.

Follow-up questions 1 and 2 can be used here to check students' understanding and help them see the relation between tables, graphs, and rules.

The following is a discussion from one classroom. The teacher pursued this question because it gave her an opportunity to review fraction and decimal ideas and operations and to help students make some new sense of what the numbers that they were calculating meant.

Teacher How did you find your solution for 2b?

George I first drew a line and put 0 at one end and 310 at the other end.

Teacher Would you go to the board and show us what you did and then continue your explanation? *(George goes to the board, draws a line segment, and labels the left end 0 and the right end 310.)*

George Then I found where halfway down the line was. *(He puts a mark at the midpoint of the line segment.)* Then I figured out that this had to be 155 because 155 is half of 310 miles.

Then I found half of each half, which is a fourth *(puts marks at both of these spots)*. Now, if each of these is half of the half, then the first mark has to be half of 155, which is 77.5 miles; and halfway between 155 and 310 has to be 232.5 miles because it has to be 77.5 miles more than 155.

Teacher Why did you put in the marks that you did and what do they show?

George I did this because I need to find how long it would take to go $\frac{3}{4}$ of the way from Williamsburg to Philadelphia, and what my drawing shows is that $\frac{3}{4}$ of the way between those cities is 232.5 miles. When I knew that, I used my table and graph to figure out how long it would take to go that far. Since it takes 4 hours to go 220 miles and I figured it takes 4.5 hours to go 247.5 miles, it has to take somewhere between 4 and 4.5 hours to go 232.5 miles. Halfway between those two times is $4\frac{1}{4}$ hours and halfway between 220 and 247.5 is 233.75 miles, so I think it takes just under $4\frac{1}{4}$ hours. Maybe like 4 hours and 14 minutes.

Teacher How did you find 233.75 miles for 4 hours 15 minutes, and why do you think that 4 hours 14 minutes is reasonable?

George Well, for each half hour you go 27.5, which is half of 55. Half of a half is a quarter so for each quarter of an hour they travel 13.75 miles. To go $4\frac{1}{4}$ hours you add 13.75 to 220. Now, because 233.75 miles is really close to 232.5 miles, I figure the times have to be close. And because 232.5 is less than 233.75, I figure the time has to be less but only a little bit. So a little bit less than 4 hours 15 minutes is 4 hours 14 minutes.

Teacher What do others think? Is what George has presented reasonable? Do you agree with him?

Amy I agree with him that $\frac{3}{4}$ of the way is 232.5 miles, but I don't think that the time is 4 hours and 14 minutes.

Teacher Explain why. Did you find something different?

Amy Yes. I got the 232.5 by multiplying 310 by 0.75. I remembered that $\frac{3}{4}$ is the same as the decimal 0.75. I also remember that if I want to find $\frac{3}{4}$ or 0.75 of something, I can do that by multiplying. So, when I entered 0.75 times 310 on my calculator, I got 232.5, the same as George. But to figure out how long it would take to go 232.5 miles, I just divided 232.5 by 55 and got 4.2272727. I'm not sure what it means. At first I thought it meant about 4 hours and 22 or 23 minutes, but what George has said makes me think that is wrong. It has to be less than 4 hours and 15 minutes, but I don't know how to figure that.

Teacher What do others think? *(silence)* Can we all agree that $\frac{3}{4}$ of the way is 232.5 miles? *(Class says yes.)* We have been shown two different ways that people thought about this, and both got the same answer and both seem reasonable. Can we also agree that it has to be around 4 hours and 15 minutes, a little less than that? *(Class agrees.)* We are still struggling with how much less and what 4.2272727 means on Amy's calculator.

(Teacher talks and writes the following on the board.) This is what I was thinking. First, I think George is very close. At 4 hours and 15 minutes, he has only gone 1.25 miles further than what we need. So 4 hours and 15 minutes or 4 hours and 14 minutes seems really close. I also have been thinking about what Amy's calculator means when it reads 4.2272727. I rounded the number to 4.23 because it is easy for me to think about decimal numbers two places after the decimal. I know that 4.23 means 4 and 23 hundredths. I can write that as $4\frac{23}{100}$. What this tells me is that it takes 4 hours and $\frac{23}{100}$ of another hour. I also know that 4 hours and 15 minutes can be written as $4\frac{25}{100}$ of an hour because 15 minutes is a fourth of an hour and a fourth is the same as $\frac{25}{100}$. Looking at the numbers that way, it seems to me that Amy has the same answer as George. Both have answers that are a bit less than 4 hours and 15 minutes.

4.2 • Changing Speeds

In this problem, students compare the travel times of a van going to Philadelphia at speeds of 65 miles per hour, 50 miles per hour, and 55 miles per hour. The main focus of the problem is finding, writing, and using rules. This provides an informal introduction to comparing slopes of lines; the idea of slope will be developed more formally in the unit *Moving Straight Ahead.*

Launch

Read the introduction to the problem. Ask students to make conjectures about the difference in time to complete the trip with speeds of 50 miles per hour and 65 miles per hour. Make sure they understand that they are to put both of these data sets onto one graph and add the data for a speed of 55 miles per hour (from Problem 4.1) using different colors. Then read Problem 4.2.

Explore

Students should work independently making their own tables and graphs as requested in part A. Students may work on the other parts of this problem and the follow-up questions in pairs. As students work, you may want to ask them which representation helps them compare the three speeds most effectively—the tables or the graph.

Summarize

Discuss parts B and C of the problem. Students should notice that the time intervals are the same for all three tables. They should also notice that even though the rates are different, the amount of change between intervals is constant. Data points for each table fall on a straight line, but each line has a different steepness.

Record students' rules for part D, question 1 on the board. Discuss the similarities and differences in these rules as well as their reasonableness. Eliminate those that do not represent the pattern of change given in the table and graph. Then use symbols to rewrite each remaining rule. Repeat this procedure for part E. You may wish to extend the discussion by asking students what rule they would write to calculate the distance traveled for any given time when riding a bike at a constant speed of 8 miles per hour. Discuss follow-up question 1 as another check of their understanding of rules.

Have students answer follow-up question 2 and explain how they found their solution. Listen for students who divide 310 by the speed (65, 60, or 50) to see that they interpret the decimal correctly. If none of the students realize that in the equation they are looking for the value of t rather than the value of d, bring the idea into the conversation. You may wish to use this dialogue to introduce the use of variables.

> To find the times for the three speeds, I thought about using the equations $d = 65t$, $d = 50t$, and $d = 55t$. What was different about this problem from others is that this time I knew the distance and had to find the time. In creating the tables, I had times and had to find the distance for each of the given times. To do this problem I filled in the d of the equation and wrote *(teacher writes on board)*:
>
> $$310 = 65t \qquad 310 = 50t \qquad 310 = 55t$$
>
> Looking at the problem this way, I realized that all I had to do to find the time was find what number I multiplied 65 by to get 310. To find the number I multiply by, I just have to divide because division is the opposite, or inverse, of multiplication. It will tell me what to multiply 65 by so that I get 310. Sometimes it helps to think of division as an operation to "undo" multiplication and vice versa. The same process is true for the other two equations.

4.3 • Calculating Costs and Profits

This problem has students revisiting Problem 3.4 to use symbols to write rules for calculating costs and profit for the tour. This is a good problem to just give to students and see what they can do with it. It should tell you whether they can write rules using symbols.

Launch

Read the introduction and the problem with your students. Remind them that they should have rules written in words for each of the situations asked in the table. If they are having trouble, you will want to find some additional problems for them to work on and to discuss as a class. The ACE questions and the Question Bank are sources of additional problems.

Explore

Have students work in pairs with each keeping a record of their solutions.

Ask students having difficulty to read the rule for finding total cost written in words from their work from Problem 3.4 part C. Continue to guide them in their exploration by asking how to represent a word or group of words with a symbol.

Summarize

The problem asks for several rules, which become more complicated as the problem proceeds. Have volunteers record their rules on the board until all variations are recorded. Have students decide which rules are correct and reasonable and explain why. It is important to discuss how incorrect rules could be revised so that students can understand their misconceptions.

For the follow-up questions, have students state their choice. After all students have given their decision, have students explain their choices. Ask the class if the explanations are reasonable and if anyone wants to change his or her answer based on a convincing explanation for a different choice. Continue the conversation until the class agrees on the one correct choice for questions 1 and 2. There are two correct choices for question 3, c and d. You may wish to use this question as an opportunity to introduce or touch upon how parentheses are used and how to read and interpret rules that use these symbols. The use and rules of order of operations are discussed and used extensively later, in the unit *Say It with Symbols*.

Additional Answers

Answers to Problem 4.1

A. Rate = 55 miles per hour

Time (hours)	Distance (miles)
0	0
1	55
2	110
3	165
4	220
5	275
6	330
7	385
8	440

Answers to Problem 4.2

A. Rate = 50 miles per hour

Rate = 65 miles per hour

Time (hours)	Distance (miles)
0	0
1	50
2	100
3	150
4	200
5	250
6	300
7	350
8	400

Time (hours)	Distance (miles)
0	0
1	65
2	130
3	195
4	260
5	325
6	390
7	455
8	520

Time and Distance Data

- - - 65 miles per hour
——— 55 miles per hour
- - - - 50 miles per hour

B. The tables are similar because the time intervals are the same and the number of miles for each set of data increases by a regular amount for each hour. They differ in the amount of the increase.

C. The graphs are similar in that all three are straight lines that rise over time. They differ in their steepness.

D. 1. The total distance traveled increases by 65 miles for each hour of time. To find the distance traveled for any given time, you multiply 65 by the number of hours.

    2. $d = 65t$

E. 1. To find the distance traveled for any given time, you multiply 50 by the number of hours.

    2. $d = 50t$

F. They all are of the form $d = rt$. The rate is different for the three rules.

ACE Answers

Applications

1a. Answers will vary. Most students will choose to make a table with intervals of 0.5 hours or 1 hour.

Time (hours)	Distance (miles)
0.0	0
0.5	30
1.0	60
1.5	90
2.0	120
2.5	150
3.0	180
3.5	210
4.0	240
4.5	270
5.0	300
5.5	330
6.0	360
6.5	390
7.0	420
7.5	450
8.0	480
8.5	510
9.0	540
9.5	570

or

Time (hours)	Distance (miles)
0	0
1	60
2	120
3	180
4	240
5	300
6	360
7	420
8	480
9	540
10	600

Basketball Road Trip

2b.

Traveling at 70 Miles per Hour

Distance (miles) vs *Time (hours)*

Connections

11c.

Number of weeks	Amount owed
0	$315
1	290
2	265
3	240
4	215
5	190
6	165
7	140
8	115
9	90
10	65
11	40
12	15
13	−10

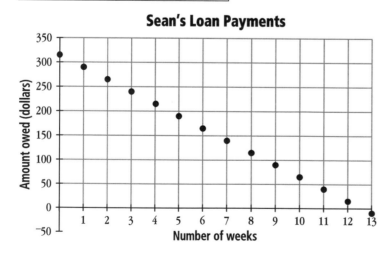

Sean's Loan Payments

Amount owed (dollars) vs *Number of weeks*

Extensions

13b. As the speed increases, the time decreases. As the speed decreases, the time increases.

For the Teacher: Considering Variable Rate

This question is intended to prompt students to begin thinking about what would happen if the *rate* or *speed* varies rather than the time or distance. Up to this point in the unit all of the problems have given a constant rate and asked one of the following questions: 1) What happens to the *distance* as *time* varies? or 2) What happens to the *time* as *distance* varies? The answers to both of these questions show a straight line when graphed. However, if the distance is held constant and the *rate* is varied, the relationships change. This problem asks the students to consider the following relationship: $40 = rt$ or $\frac{40}{r} = t$. Its graph is as follows:

40-mile Trip

As the graph shows, as *rate* increases, *time* decreases, and as *rate* decreases, *time* increases. However, the relationship is not linear. In other words, the change is not a steady change. This problem may be your students' first encounter with a nonlinear relationship between two variables, expressed as an equation.

Using a Graphing Calculator

Prior investigations have helped students become comfortable with graphs, tables, and writing simple rules that represent the relationship between two variables. Graphing calculators are introduced at this point to give students the opportunity to work with the technology. Students are often surprised that the calculator knows how to make an entire table or graph if a person enters in a symbolic rule. This powerful feature makes the graphing calculator a useful tool for analyzing situations involving variables. Since the language of communication with the calculator is symbolic, students see a benefit in being able to write symbolic rules to describe situations. In Problem 5.1, Graphing on a Calculator, students use graphing calculators to compare the graphs of various equations. Problem 5.2, Making Tables on a Calculator, has students using the graphing calculator to make tables and then using the tables to find values of x when given a value of y.

Mathematical and Problem-Solving Goals

- **To use a rule to generate a table or graph on the graphing calculator**

- **To use a graphing calculator to compare the tables and graphs of various rules; in particular, to decide whether a given rule defines a straight-line (linear) function by examining graphs**

Materials		
Problem	For students	For the teacher
All	Graphing calculators, grid paper (provided as a black-line master)	Transparencies 5.1 to 5.2 (optional), overhead display model of the students' graphing calculator (optional), linking software to allow printing of calculator screens and copying features of calculator screens into printed documents (optional)
5.1	Labsheet 5.1 (2 per group; optional)	

INVESTIGATION 5

Using a Graphing Calculator

In the last investigation, you wrote equations to describe patterns and to show how variables are related. Such equations are used in mathematics, science, economics, and many other subject areas. So far, you have written equations that fit the patterns you observed in tables and graphs. Sometimes, you will need to create a table or graph that fits a given equation. In this investigation, you will use a tool called a *graphing calculator* to make graphs and tables that fit a given equation.

5.1 Graphing on a Calculator

The organizers of the Ocean and History Bike Tour need to bring spare parts in the van in case any of the customers have problems with their bikes. They think they will have enough tires if they bring two spare tires for each customer. Theo wrote this rule as the equation $t = 2c$, where t is the number of spare tires needed for c customers.

You can use a graphing calculator to make a graph of Theo's equation. To use a calculator to make graphs and tables, you need to type in an equation that uses the letters y and x to represent the variables. We write these equations so that x is the independent variable and y is the dependent variable. Rewriting Theo's equation using x and y, we get $y = 2x$, where y is the number of tires needed for x customers.

When you press the $\boxed{Y=}$ button, you get a screen like the one below. The calculator gives the "$y =$" part of the equation; you need to type in the rest. You can enter Theo's equation, $y = 2x$, by pressing $\boxed{2}$, followed by the letter $\boxed{X}$.

```
Y1=2X
Y2=
Y3=
Y4=
```

Graphing on a Calculator

At a Glance

*Grouping:
small groups*

Launch

- Check settings on all graphing calculators.
- Discuss how to rewrite equations using x and y.
- Have students follow the key sequences in the introduction and discuss the resulting graph.

Explore

- Remind students to sketch their graphs on Labsheet 5.1.
- Assign the follow-up questions.

Summarize

- Discuss the similarities and differences in the graphs.
- Extend the discussion by having students give a new rule to fit each pattern and use their graphing calculators to check their prediction.
- Have students explain how to find the values of y in the follow-up questions.

Assignment Choices

ACE questions 3, 4, 6, and unassigned choices from earlier problems

After you enter the equation, press GRAPH to see the graph. Here is the graph of $y = 2x$.

Problem 5.1

Experiment with your graphing calculator and the following equations. Graph one set of equations at a time. For each set, two of the graphs will be similar in some way, and one of the graphs will be different. Answer questions A and B for each set.

Set 1:	$y = 3x - 4$	$y = x^2$	$y = 3x + 2$
Set 2:	$y = 5$	$y = 3x$	$y = 1x$
Set 3:	$y = 2x + 3$	$y = 2x - 5$	$y = 0.5x + 2$
Set 4:	$y = 2x$	$y = 2 \div x$	$y = x + 5$

A. 1. Which two equations in the set have graphs that are similar?

  2. In what ways are the two graphs similar?

  3. In what ways are the equations for the two graphs similar?

B. 1. Which equation in the set has a graph that is different from the graphs of the other equations?

  2. In what way is the graph different from the other graphs?

  3. In what way is the equation different from the other equations?

■ Problem 5.1 Follow-Up

1. Use the equation $y = 2x$ to answer the following questions.
  a. If $x = 2$, what is y?
  b. If $x = \frac{2}{3}$, what is y?
  c. If $x = 3.25$, what is y?
  d. You can make a table to show pairs of numbers that fit an equation. Complete the following table for the equation $y = 2x$.

x	0	1	2	3	4	5	6
y							

62 Variables and Patterns

Answers to Problem 5.1

See page 68d.

Answers to Problem 5.1 Follow-Up

1. **a.** $y = 4$ **b.** $y = \frac{4}{3}$ **c.** $y = 6.5$

  d.

x	0	1	2	3	4	5	6
y	0	2	4	6	8	10	12

2.

x	0	1	2	3	4	5	6
y	3	5	7	9	11	13	15

3. For both tables, the value for y increases by 2 as you move across the table.

2. Complete the following table for the equation $y = 2x + 3$.

x	0	1	2	3	4	5	6
y							

3. How is the table for $y = 2x + 3$ in question 2 similar to the table for $y = 2x$ in question 1?

5.2 Making Tables on a Calculator

Some graphing calculators can create tables of data for an equation. To use your calculator to create a table, first press $\boxed{Y=}$ and type in an equation. Then, press $\boxed{TABLE}$ to see the table for that equation. Here is part of the table for the equation $y = 2x$.

X	Y1
0	0
1	2
2	4
3	6
4	8
5	10

X=0

Problem 5.2

A. 1. Use your calculator to make a table for the equation $y = 3x$.

   2. Copy part of the calculator's table onto your paper.

   3. Use your table to find y if $x = 5$.

B. 1. Use your calculator to make a table for the equation $y = 0.5x + 2$.

   2. Copy part of the calculator's table onto your paper.

   3. Use your table to find y if $x = 5$.

■ Problem 5.2 Follow-Up

1. Use your calculator to make a graph for the equation $y = 3x$. Describe the graph.

2. Use your calculator to make a graph for the equation $y = 0.5x + 2$. Describe the graph.

3. How do the graphs for questions 1 and 2 compare?

4. How would you make a graph for the equations $y = 3x$ and $y = 0.5x + 2$ without a graphing calculator?

At a Glance

Grouping: small groups

Launch

■ Have students use graphing calculators to make tables from rules. (Not all graphing calculators have this function.)

Explore

■ Have students work in groups of two or three. Each student needs to have a record of his or her answer.

■ Circulate, helping students who are having trouble.

■ Use the follow-up questions to integrate students' knowledge of tables and graphs.

Summarize

■ Have students share tables and explain how they found the y value for a given value of x.

■ Encourage students to describe and compare the graphs in the follow-up questions.

Answers to Problem 5.2

See page 68e.

Answers to Problem 5.2 Follow-Up

1. Possible answer: It is a straight line.

2. Possible answer: It is a straight line.

3. Possible answer: Both graphs are straight lines, and the graph of $y = 3x$ is steeper.

4. Answers will vary but should relate to making a table of x and y values for each equation, plotting those points, and connecting them with a line.

Assignment Choices

ACE questions 1, 2, 5, 7, and unassigned choices from earlier problems (question 7 requires grid paper)

Answers

Applications

1a. If $x = 5$, $y = 2.5$.

1b. See below right.

1c. $y = \frac{1}{2}x$

2. Possible answer: (1, 4), (2, 8), (3, 12); Students can determine these values from the graph or equation using a method similar to that discussed in question 1b.

As you work on these ACE questions, use your calculator whenever you need it.

Applications

1. Trevor entered an equation into his graphing calculator, and it displayed this table and graph.

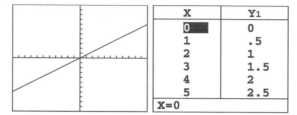

X	Y1
0	0
1	.5
2	1
3	1.5
4	2
5	2.5
X=0	

a. If $x = 5$, what is y?

b. How is this shown on the table? On the graph?

c. What equation did Trevor enter into his calculator?

2. Ziamara used her calculator to make a graph of the equation $y = 4x$. She noticed that the point (0, 0) was on the graph. Name three other points that are on the graph. Explain how you found these points.

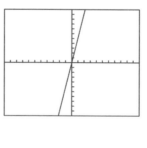

1b. In the table, the 5 in the x column corresponds to the 2.5 in the y column. From the graph, students can read the point as shown below.

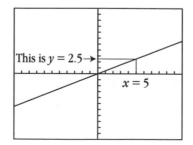

This is $y = 2.5$ →

$x = 5$

3. Each of the following tables shows how two variables are related. Find a pattern in each table. Use the pattern to complete the missing entries. Express the rule for the pattern as an equation, using the given letters as variable names.

a.

A	0	1	2	3		8	20	100
B	0	7	14	21	28			

b.

X	0	1	2	3	4	8	20	100
Y	6	7	8	9				

c.

X	0	1	2	3	4	8	20	100
Y	1	3	5	7				

d.

R	0	1	2	3	4	6	10	20
S	0	1	4	9	16			

Connections

4. You have seen that many of the costs for the Ocean and History Bike Tour depend on the number of customers. This table shows the relationship between the number of customers and the cost of the ferry ride from Cape May, New Jersey, to Lewes, Delaware.

Customers	1	2	3	4	5	6	7	8	9
Ferry cost	$2.50	5.00	7.50	10.00	12.50	15.00	17.50	20.00	22.50

a. Write an equation relating ferry cost, f, and number of customers, n.

b. Use your equation to find the cost if 35 people are on the tour.

c. How many people could cross on the ferry if the tour leader had $75?

3. See below left.

Connections

4a. $f = 2.50n$

4b. $87.50; since $f = 2.50 \times 35$, $f = 87.50$

4c. 30 people; $75 = 2.50n$, so $n = \frac{75}{2.50}$, so $n = 30$

3a. $B = 7A$

A	0	1	2	3	4	8	20	100
B	0	7	14	21	28	56	140	700

3b. $Y = X + 6$

X	0	1	2	3	4	8	20	100
Y	6	7	8	9	10	14	26	106

3c. $Y = 2X + 1$

X	0	1	2	3	4	8	20	100
Y	1	3	5	7	9	17	41	201

3d. $S = R^2$

R	0	1	2	3	4	6	10	20
S	0	1	4	9	16	36	100	400

![ACE]

5. Yes, these data could be represented in a table because there are corresponding x and y values. It could not be stated with a rule because there is not a predictable pattern that can be expressed by a simple rule.

6a. $A = lw$; $P = 2l + 2w$ or $P = 2(l + w)$ or $P = l + w + l + w$

6b. $A = bh$; $P = 2b + 2s$

6c. $A = \frac{1}{2}bh$; $P = a + b + c$

5. Look back at question 4 on page 28 in Investigation 2. The first graph shows the relationship between Amanda's hunger and the time of day. Could you represent this relationship in a table? Could you represent this relationship with an equation? Explain your reasoning.

6. The rules for calculating area and perimeter for common polygons are often written with symbols. Using A for area, P for perimeter, b for base, h for height, l for length, and w for width, write equations for the rules for finding the area and perimeter of each figure below. These equations are usually called *formulas*.

a.

b.

c.

Extensions

7. When the tour partners had a 30-mile race on the last day, they gave the two young riders, Tony and Sarah, a half-hour head start. For this first half hour, Tony and Sarah rode at a steady pace of 12 miles per hour. After their half-hour head start, they kept up a fairly steady pace of about 10 miles per hour. When the others started riding, they went at a fairly steady pace of about 15 miles per hour.

a. Make a table and a graph showing the relationship between distance and time for each group of riders.

b. Will the older riders catch up with Tony and Sarah before the end of the 30-mile race? Explain your answer using both the tables and the graphs.

c. Use *d* for distance traveled (in miles) and *t* for riding time (in hours) from when the second group started riding to write equations showing the relationship between these two variables for

i. Tony and Sarah **ii.** The other riders

Extensions

7a. See page 68e.

7b. Yes, this can be noticed on the table after 1.25 hours when the other riders have traveled farther than Tony and Sarah. On the graph, this can be seen where the two lines cross. This is the point at which the other riders meet Tony and Sarah.

7c. i. $d = 6 + 10t$
ii. $d = 15t$

Possible Answers

1. Answers will vary. Students may decide on their equations and then follow the general directions given in Problem 5.1 to make a graph and the directions given in Problem 5.2 to make a table.

2a. $t = \frac{1}{2}c$, where t = number of tents and c = number of customers

2b. Yes. This question is intended to check students' understanding and appreciation of the fact that one simple rule can give us a large amount of data (an infinite amount in this case). The rule $t = \frac{1}{2}c$ actually gives us more information than any table or graph could, since a table and a graph only give information for a small range of values, while the rule tells us the relationship between t and c for any value.

3. Answers will vary. Some examples might be someone's feelings of hunger or happiness over time, temperature changes over time, or amount of rainfall over time. These will either be a case where the pattern is not very regular and therefore a rule is impossible to write or just an example of where students have not yet had experiences with rules.

Mathematical Reflections

In this investigation, you learned how to use a graphing calculator to make graphs and tables from equations. These questions will help you summarize what you have learned:

1 Write a letter to a friend explaining how to use a graphing calculator to make graphs and tables. Use a specific example to illustrate your explanation.

2 The number of tents the tour organizers need is $\frac{1}{2}$ times the number of customers.

    a. Write an equation for a rule you can use to calculate the number of tents for any number of customers.

    b. Does your equation give you enough information to make a table and a graph? Why or why not?

3 Think of a situation for which you can make a graph and a table, but not an equation.

Think about your answers to these questions, discuss your ideas with other students and your teacher, and then write a summary of your findings in your journal.

68 Variables and Patterns

Tips for the Linguistically Diverse Classroom

Diagram Code The Diagram Code technique is described in detail in *Getting to Know Connected Mathematics*. Students use a minimal number of words and drawings, diagrams, or symbols to respond to questions that require writing. Example: Question 3—A student might respond by drawing an *x*-axis labeled time (or by drawing a calendar) and a *y*-axis labeled rainfall (or by drawing a dark rain cloud with rain coming from it).

TEACHING THE INVESTIGATION

5.1 • Graphing on a Calculator

This problem allows students to explore graphing calculators. Students explore what shape different equations produce on the graph and look for patterns between equations that produce a similar shape.

Launch

Students may need direction in using the calculator. You may find it helpful to set some ground rules about distributing and collecting the graphing calculators as well as how they are treated. If this is the first time that your students have worked with graphing calculators, you may wish to give students some time to familiarize themselves with the calculators and to discover how different they are from basic calculators.

For the Teacher: Adjusting Calculator Settings

Because you will want all students to have the same table and graph on their calculators, you may wish to begin by either checking that all the calculators are using the same default setting or by having the class adjust the settings on their calculators as shown in the "Setup Notes" below. (Note: Settings for Texas Instruments TI-80 and TI-82 calculators are shown. If another calculator is used, see your reference manual for instructions.)

Setup Notes

1. Put the calculator into Normal mode. Do this by pressing [MODE], then using the cursor and [ENTER] keys to darken everything on the left side until all settings are the same as in the picture at the right.

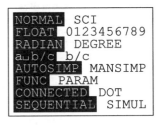

2. Adjust the TABLE SETUP by pressing [2ND], then [WINDOW]. (At the top of the WINDOW key, it says TblSet.) Use the cursor key to adjust the settings to match the picture at the right.

```
TABLE SETUP
  TblMin=0
  △Tbl=1
```

3. Turn off STAT PLOTS. (At this point in the curriculum, students do not need to know what this key does, but they do need to turn it off since it can cause mischief on their graph screens.) "STAT PLOT" is above the $\boxed{Y=}$ key, so is accessed by pressing $\boxed{2ND}$ then $\boxed{Y=}$. Turn Plots Off by either selecting 4: PLOTSOFF and pressing $\boxed{ENTER}$ or by pressing $\boxed{4}$ then $\boxed{ENTER}$.

 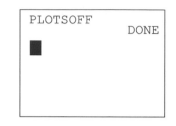

4. Press $\boxed{Y=}$, and use the $\boxed{CLEAR}$ and $\boxed{ENTER}$ buttons to erase any functions that may have previously been entered.

```
Y1=
Y2=
Y3=
Y4=
```

5. Press $\boxed{ZOOM}$, and select 6: ZSTANDARD to set the default range for graphing.

```
ZOOM
1:ZBOX
2:ZOOM IN
3:ZOOM OUT
4:ZDECIMAL
5:ZSQUARE
6:ZSTANDARD
7:ZTRIG
```

```
ZOOM
1:ZBOX
2:ZOOM IN
3:ZOOM OUT
4:ZDECIMAL
5:ZSQUARE
6:ZSTANDARD
7:ZTRIG
```

Have the students put the calculators to the side and read through the first two paragraphs of the introduction to the problem. Make sure students understand how rules that are written with variables other than x and y can be rewritten using x as the independent value and y as the dependent value.

Read the final part of the introduction aloud as students enter the given sequence or the sequence needed for the type of calculator your students are using. After they watch their calculators perform the graphing, have them compare the graph with the picture in the text. These graphs differ from others in this book since they show all four quadrants. Although we are not formally introducing negative numbers at this time, students' experience with concepts such as "below zero" and "in the hole" will be sufficient for making sense of these graphs.

Have neighbors help those having difficulty redo their graphs. To provide students with another opportunity to graph on their calculator, write a new rule, such as $y = x$, on the board. Have students enter it into their calculator and then graph. Ask the following questions.

What is the shape of the graph for $y = x$? *(a straight line)*

What was the shape of the graph for $y = 2x$? *(a straight line)*

How are the two lines different? *(The line for y = 2x is steeper than the line for y = x.)*

Have students make conjectures about the graphs of these two rules.

What do you think the graph of *y = 3x* will look like? How about *y = x + 3*? *(You want students to notice that y = 3x is steeper than either y = x or y = 2x and that y = x + 3 has the same steepness as y = x and that it is moved up on the graph, parallel to y = x.)*

Once students know how to enter rules and graph equations, have them work on Problem 5.1. Have students enter one graph at a time on their calculators and make a sketch of each graph on Labsheet 5.1 (blank graphing calculator screens). Remind students what an exponent means, and show them how to enter an exponent for $y = x^2$.

Explore

Have students work in groups of two or three. Suggest that students having difficulty think about the shapes of the graphs and how they change when scanned from left to right across the graph. As students finish with the problem, have them work on the follow-up questions.

Summarize

This problem asks students to take a global look at some rules and what happens when they are graphed. Discuss the similarities and differences among the graphs. You may wish to have students use an overhead graphing calculator if one is available to help make their points. When students discuss the similarities between two of the rules in a set, ask them if they could give a new rule that would fit the pattern they have described. Then have the class use their calculators to check the graph of that rule. If your students can find patterns in rules and make correct predictions for new rules that work in each of the sets, continue the discussion and explore the effects of the coefficient of x in the equations $y = mx$ or $y = mx + b$. These ideas will be explored in depth in the *Moving Straight Ahead* unit.

Discuss the follow-up questions. Invite students to explain how they found the values for y in parts a, b, and c of question 1. Review the tables in question 1d and in question 2. An understanding of how to generate tables from rules is needed for Problem 5.2.

5.2 • Making Tables on a Calculator

The purpose of this problem is to show students how the graphing calculator will create tables for a given rule. Check to see if your graphing calculators have this function (some do not).

Launch

Read the introduction with your students. As the text describes how to make a table with the calculator, have students enter the given sequence (or the sequence needed for the type of calculator your students are using) and compare their table to the one shown. Have volunteers help students who were unsuccessful in this first attempt to produce the table.

Have students work on Problem 5.2 and the follow-up questions in groups of two or three.

Explore

In the follow-up questions, students review skills taught in Problem 5.1 and integrate their knowledge of table and graph representations.

Summarize

Have students share their tables and explain how they found the values of y for question 3 of both parts A and B. The follow-up questions review the ideas discussed in Problem 5.1. This will be a good check to see what sense students have made of their graphing calculator experience.

Additional Answers

Answers to Problem 5.1

A. Set 1
    1. $y = 3x - 4$ and $y = 3x + 2$
    2. Both graphs are straight lines, and the lines are parallel.
    3. Both have x multiplied by 3.

    Set 2
    1. $y = 3x$ and $y = 1x$
    2. Both graphs are straight lines that pass through (0, 0).
    3. Both have x in them, and the x is being multiplied by a number.

    Set 3
    1. $y = 2x + 3$ and $y = 2x - 5$
    2. The graphs have the same steepness (they are parallel).
    3. Both have x multiplied by 2.

    Set 4
    1. $y = 2x$ and $y = x + 5$
    2. The graphs are straight lines.
    3. Both equations involve a multiple of x (the multiple in $y = x + 5$ is 1).

B. Set 1
    1. $y = x^2$
    2. The graph is a curve instead of a straight line.
    3. The x is squared in this equation and not in the others.

    Set 2
    1. $y = 5$
    2. It is a horizontal line and has no steepness. It is flat.
    3. It doesn't have an x variable.

    Set 3
    1. $y = 0.5x + 2$
    2. It has a different steepness than the other two. It isn't as steep.
    3. The x is multiplied by 0.5 instead of by 2.

    Set 4
    1. $y = 2 \div x$
    2. The graph is two curves.
    3. The equation has a number divided by x.

Answers to Problem 5.2

A. 1–2.

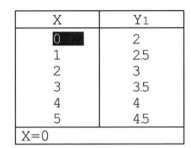

X	Y1
0	0
1	3
2	6
3	9
4	12
5	15
X=0	

3. For $x = 5$, $y = 15$.

B. 1–2.

X	Y1
0	2
1	2.5
2	3
3	3.5
4	4
5	4.5
X=0	

3. For $x = 5$, $y = 4.5$.

ACE Answers

Extensions

7a. Tables will vary, but should approximate the one shown.

Time (hours)	0	0.25	0.5	0.75	1	1.25	1.5	1.75	2
Distance (Tony and Sarah)	6	8.5	11	13.5	16	18.5	21	23.5	26
Distance (others)	0	3.75	7.5	11.25	15	18.75	22.5	26.25	30

30-mile Race

— Tony and Sarah

- - - - Others

Answers

Using Your Algebraic Reasoning

1a. Accept any reasonable factor such as weight, distance, size of the package, value of the package, fragility of the contents, and speed of delivery.

b. Answers will depend on the variables mentioned by students. Expect statements such as "The farther a package is sent, the greater the cost" or "The faster delivery is to occur, the greater the cost."

2a,b See the bottom of page 68g.

Unit Reflections

Working on the problems of this unit, you explored some of the big ideas in algebra. You learned how to identify *variables*, quantities that change in value as time passes or in response to change in other quantities. You learned how to collect and display data in *tables* and *coordinate graphs*, how to look for patterns relating *independent* and *dependent variables*, and how to express those patterns in words and in *equations* or *formulas*. Most important of all, you learned how to study tables, graphs, and equations to answer questions about variables.

Using Your Algebraic Reasoning—To test your understanding and skill in use of algebraic ideas and techniques, consider an example of how algebra is involved in a business that we all use or depend on—the shipping of packages from town to town, across the country, and around the world.

1 *When you take a package to the post office or to a package-shipping company, one big concern is the cost for shipping and insuring the package.*

a. List at least three variables that will affect the cost of shipping a package.

b. For each variable you list, explain its effect on the shipping cost.

2 *Suppose that a service offers to ship any package weighing at most two pounds to any place in the United States in two days or less for a price that depends on distance. The total charge is a $5 handling fee plus $0.01 for each mile that the package is carried.*

a. Copy and complete the table of sample shipping charges for such packages:

Distance in miles	100	200	300	400	500	1000	1500	2000
Shipping Cost								

Describe the pattern by which shipping cost increases as shipping distance increases.

b. Use grid paper to make a graph showing shipping charges for any distance between 0 and 2000 miles. Use appropriate labels and scales on the axes.

How to Use
Looking Back and Looking Ahead: Unit Reflections

The first part of this section includes problems that allow students to demonstrate their mathematical understandings and skills. The second part gives them an opportunity to explain their reasoning. This section can be used as a review to help students stand back and reflect on the "big" ideas and connections in the unit. This section may be assigned as homework, followed up with class discussion the next day. Focus on the *Explaining Your Reasoning* section in the discussion. Encourage the students to refer to the problems to illustrate their reasoning.

c. Write an equation or formula that gives the relation between distance, *d*, in miles and shipping cost, *C*, in dollars for this special rate.

d. Use a graphing calculator and the rule in part c to check your answers to part a and part b.

e. Use one or more of the tools you have—rule, table, graph, equation, and calculator—to answer these questions about shipping cost.

    i. What is the cost for shipping a package 450 miles?

    ii. How far can you ship a two-pound package at a cost of $35 or less?

Explaining Your Reasoning—When you use mathematical calculations to solve a problem or make a decision, you should be able to justify each step in your reasoning. Answer these questions about your work on Problems 1 and 2.

1. How did you arrive at the entries in the table of shipping costs for distances from 100 to 2000 miles?

2. How did you choose labels and scales for axes on the graph of shipping cost and distance? Did you plot only data pairs falling on grid points or did you connect those points with a smooth graph? Explain your choice of graphing strategy.

3. How could you convince someone that you have the right formula relating distance and shipping cost?

4. Why did you use the table, graph, equation, or rule in words to answer the questions of Problem 2e?

5. If you were asked to write a report describing the relationship between shipping distance and cost, what might be gained by including the table? The graph? The formula? What are the limitations of each type of display in showing the relationship?

The algebra ideas and techniques you've used in this unit will be applied and extended in many future algebra units of *Connected Mathematics* such as *Moving Straight Ahead*, *Thinking with Mathematical Models*, and *Say It with Symbols*. Understanding variables and patterns is essential to your future "mathematical life" in school and in work—to solve problems in architecture, medicine, economics, computing, engineering, and statistics.

2c. $C = 5 + 0.01d$ or $C = 0.01d + 5$

  d. To use the graphing calculator, students will need to enter $y = 0.01x + 5$ and then produce tables with delta Tbl = 100. To graph, they will need to set the window boundaries at x-min = 0, x-max = 2000, y-min = 0 and y-max = 25.

  e. **i.** Cost is $5 + 0.01(450) = \$9.50$

    ii. Solve the equation $5 + 0.01d = 35$, so $d = 3000$ miles. Possible solution methods: tracing a table or graph, successive approximation, or "undoing" the calculations.

Explaining Your Reasoning
See p. 68h

2a.

Distance (miles)	100	200	300	400	500	1000	1500	2000
Shipping cost ($)	6	7	8	9	10	15	20	25

Each increase of 100 miles in distance increases the shipping cost by $1.

b.

Looking Back and Looking Ahead

Note to the Teacher

The purpose of this section of *Variables and Patterns* is to help students review and articulate the key ideas of the unit—first through work on problems that require use of the major concepts and skills and second through responses to some broader questions about the underlying mathematical principles and techniques. The students learned how to identify variables in a variety of situations. They developed understanding and skill required to collect and display data in *tables* and *coordinate graphs,* to look for patterns relating *independent* and *dependent variables,* and to express those patterns in words, in *equations,* or in *formulas.* Most important of all, they began developing skills for using tables, graphs, and equations to answer questions about variables.

This is the first unit in the *Connected Mathematics* algebra strand. The foundation is being laid, so that students develop a solid understanding of the key ideas that will continue to grow over the years ahead. In future units, students will apply key ideas in a variety of specific kinds of algebraic relationships and expressions.

Answers

Explaining Your Reasoning

1. Multiply the number of miles by the cost per mile, $0.01, and add the basic fixed handling charge of $5.

2. First, identify the independent variable for the *x*-axis (distance) and the dependent variable for the *y*-axis (cost). Then look at the range of distance and cost values that are applicable. For the tick-marks on each axis, divide the range by 10 to get the value represented by each segment on each axis. In this case, $\frac{2000}{10}$ = 200 miles per tick-mark on the *x*-axis and $\frac{25}{10}$ = 2.5 dollars per tick-mark on the *y*-axis. Possible labels on the axes are "Distance in miles" and "Cost in dollars."

3. Answers will vary. Explanations could mention using the formula to calculate a sample of prices for several different distances. A better argument would mention the need to multiply the cost per mile, $0.01, by the number of miles, *x,* and then add the fixed handling cost of $5.

4. Answers will vary, but the idea is that students explain why they prefer one approach or another. For example, some students might say that they like to search in a table because the numbers tell them specific distance and price data that they can understand. Others might prefer a graph because it shows the big picture of the relationship visually. Others might prefer equations because there is a procedure to follow directly to the answer without estimation.

5. The purpose of this question is to get students to think about the various useful mathematical tools that they are acquiring and when each is most useful. Possible answers: a graph gives a quick overall picture of a relationship, a table gives specific numerical information more directly, and a formula gives a tool for calculating outputs (*y*) for any input (*x*).

Assessment Resources

Check-Up	70
Quiz	73
Question Bank	76
Unit Test	79
Notebook Checklist	83
Self-Assessment	84
Answer Keys	85
Supporting Inclusion Students	91
Recording and Displaying Student Work	95

Check-Up

1. Stefan said he had done an experiment similar to the jumping jack exercise. He had collected data on the number of deep knee bends a person could do in 2 minutes. The graph below shows his data.

Deep Knee Bends

a. What are the two variables?

b. Make a table of Stefan's data.

c. Describe how the number of deep knee bends changes for each 10-second interval as time increases.

d. From Stefan's data, estimate the number of knee bends he did in 25 seconds and in 65 seconds. Explain how you made those estimates.

Check-Up

2. The table shows some data Carmen collected during her swim team practice.

Number of breaths	0	1	2	3	4	5	6	7
Number of meters swum	0	5	8	12	15	17	20	24

a. What are the two variables?

b. Graph the data from the table on the axes below.

c. Does it make sense to connect the points? Explain your reasoning.

Check-Up

d. When did Carmen make the most progress?

How does this show up in the table?

How does this show up in the graph?

e. When did Carmen make the least progress?

How does this show up in the table?

How does this show up in the graph?

f. How many breaths do you think she would take if she swam 50 meters?

Quiz

1. Dominic and Norm decide to save their money to go on a bike tour in their state. Dominic thinks he can save $10 per week. Norm has $25 from his birthday to start with and plans to add $7 each week.

    a. Make a table that will show the amount of money each boy will have over the next ten weeks if they stick to their plans.

    b. Use the entries in your tables to graph each boy's savings over time. Use a different color to graph the data for each boy.

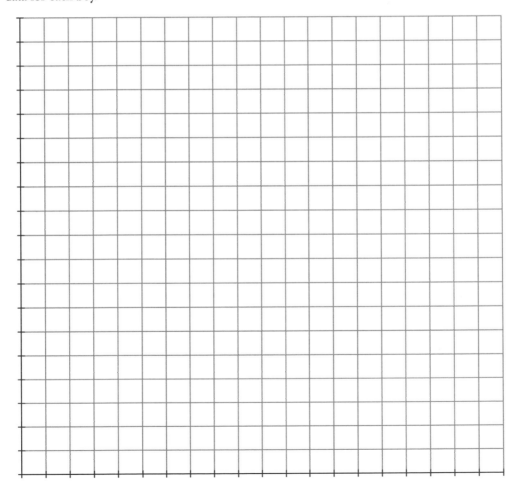

Quiz

c. Write a rule to show how much money each boy has for any number of weeks.

Dominic:

Norm:

d. Will the boys ever have the same amount of money at the same time? Explain your reasoning.

e. If the bike tour costs $190, when will each boy have enough money to go on the tour?

2. Read the following story carefully. Then, on the next page, make a table and a graph for the story.

Angie and her friend Jane are going to see a movie at the Civic Theater. The theater is eight blocks from Angie's house. Jane's house is halfway between the theater and Angie's house. Angie tells Jane that she will walk over to her house, and then they will walk the rest of the way together.

*   Angie leaves at 4:25 P.M. for a 5:00 P.M. show.
*   It takes her 10 minutes to walk to Jane's house.
*   She waits 5 minutes for Jane, and then they walk for two blocks.
*   Jane's dog Gizmo appears, so they go back to Jane's house and put Gizmo inside.
*   They are afraid of being late, so they run to get to the theater on time.
*   They arrive at 4:56 P.M., get their popcorn, and watch the show.

Names _____ Date _____

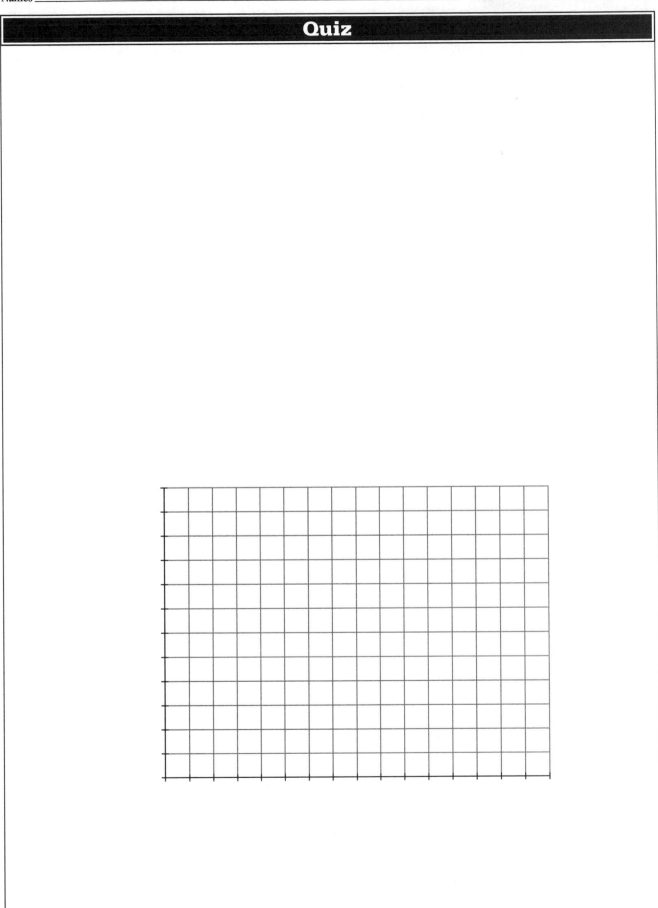

Assign these questions as additional homework, or use them as review, quiz, or test questions.

1. Teresa baby-sits for $2.50 an hour.
   a. Make a table showing how much money she will make over time.
   b. Graph your data.

   c. Does it make sense to connect the points on the graph? Why or why not?
   d. What is a rule that would let you calculate how much Teresa would make for any amount of time she worked?

2. The graph below shows data that Elizabeth collected while walking.

   a. When does she make the most progress? Explain your reasoning.
   b. When does she make the least progress? Explain your reasoning.

3. The following sketch shows the diagonals that can be drawn from one vertex of a pentagon. The diagonals split the pentagon into three triangular regions. The same sort of *triangulation* can be done in other polygons as well.

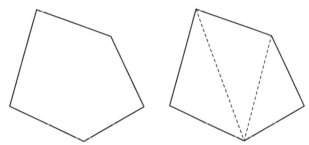

a. Draw polygons of 4, 5, 6, 7, 8, 9, and 10 sides. In each, pick one vertex and draw all possible diagonals from that vertex. Make a table to record the number of diagonals drawn in the different polygons. Leave room in your table to add another row of information from part c.

b. Find a pattern that predicts the number of diagonals that can be drawn from one vertex in a polygon. Write the pattern as a rule using *n* for the number of sides and *d* for the number of diagonals. Verify your formula using any three of the figures you sketched for part a.

c. Count the number of regions that the diagonals form in the polygons. Record your results in the table you made for part a.

d. Find a pattern relating number of sides in a polygon to the number of regions formed by drawing diagonals from one vertex. Write your pattern in symbolic form, using *n* for number of sides and *r* for number of regions formed.

e. Use the rule you wrote in part d to calculate the number of regions formed in each of the following polygons.
   i. 20 sides   ii. 50 sides   iii. 1000 sides   iv. 1,000,000 sides

4. Each day the cafeteria workers at Edison Middle School start out with 400 cartons of milk. They collected some data and made the following graph.

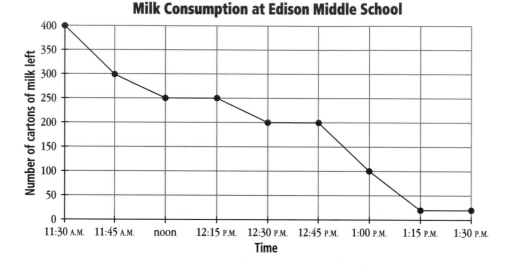

a. What is the total number of cartons of milk sold?

b. How many cartons were sold between noon and 12:30 P.M.?

c. During what 15-minute time period(s) was the most milk sold?

d. During what 15-minute time period(s) was the least amount of milk sold?

e. Describe how the total number of cartons of milk available changed as the day progressed.

f. Should the cafeteria workers have connected the points? Explain.

g. Would a table be useful? Why or why not?

Unit Test

1. Sidney, Liz, and Malcolm thought it would be a good idea to get a souvenir T-shirt for each customer who went on the Ocean and History Bike Tour. Latisha found a company who would sell them shirts with their logo for $6.95.

    a. Make a table and a graph that show number of shirts and cost.

    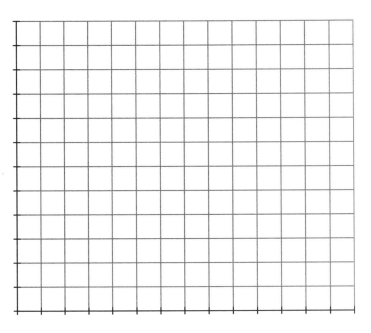

    b. Would it make sense to connect the points on your graph with a line? Why or why not?

    c. Write a rule using symbols to determine the T-shirt cost for any number of customers.

Unit Test

2. Dee bought a compact disc player with the money he earned working during his vacation. He checked CD costs at two stores.
    - Taylor's Department Store sells CDs for $15.49 each.
    - Buyer's Warehouse has a $25 membership fee, then each CD costs $12.

    a. Make a table and a graph that show the cost of purchasing several different quantities of CDs at each store.

    b. How many CDs would Dee have to purchase to have Buyer's Warehouse be the best place to buy CDs?

    c. How many CDs would Dee have to purchase to have Taylor's Department Store be the best place to buy CDs?

    d. Explain which representation—the narrative description, the table, or the graph—helps you the most in making the decision of where to buy CDs.

Unit Test

3. Hiroshi gave $y = 8x$ as the answer to a question on his test paper. Make up a situation that his rule could represent.

4. Mary and Juanita made the following graphs.

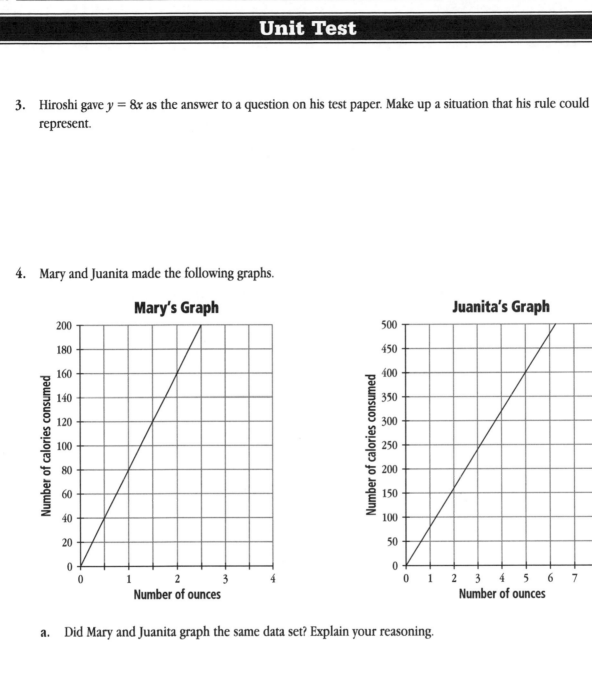

Mary's Graph

Juanita's Graph

a. Did Mary and Juanita graph the same data set? Explain your reasoning.

b. Write a rule relating the number of ounces to the calories consumed from Mary's graph.

Unit Test

5. Francisco was working on a problem on his graphing calculator. He saw the following two screens.

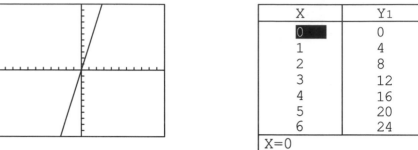

X	Y1
0	0
1	4
2	8
3	12
4	16
5	20
6	24

X=0

His partner made a sketch of the two screens. Then, he accidentally cleared the rule from the screen by pressing Y= .

a. Write a rule that would re-create this graph and table.

b. Give a situation that could be represented by your rule.

Notebook Checklist

Journal Organization

_____ Problems and Mathematical Reflections are labeled and dated.

_____ Work is neat and easy to find and follow.

Vocabulary

_____ All words are listed.

_____ All words are defined or described.

Notebook Organization

_____ Check-Up

_____ Quiz

_____ Unit Test

Homework Assignments

_____ _____

_____ _____

_____ _____

_____ _____

_____ _____

_____ _____

_____ _____

_____ _____

_____ _____

_____ _____

_____ _____

_____ _____

_____ _____

Name _____ Date _____

Vocabulary

Of the vocabulary words that I defined or described in my journal, the word _____ best demonstrates my ability to give a clear and complete definition or description.

Of the vocabulary words that I defined or described in my journal, the word _____ best demonstrates my ability to use an example to help explain or describe an idea.

Mathematical Ideas

1. a. In *Variables and Patterns,* I learned these things about variables and patterns as well as how tables, graphs, and rules can help me find and describe patterns:

    b. Here are page numbers of journal entries that give evidence of what I have learned, along with descriptions of what each entry shows:

2. a. The mathematical ideas that I am still struggling with:

    b. This is why I think these ideas are difficult for me:

    c. Here are page numbers of journal entries that give evidence of what I am struggling with, along with descriptions of what each entry shows:

Class Participation

I contributed to the classroom discussion and understanding of *Variables and Patterns* when I . . .
(Give examples.)

Answers to the Check-Up

1. **a.** Number of seconds and total number of knee bends

    b. Answers will vary, but they should be close to those given in the table.

Time (seconds)	10	20	30	40	50	60	70	80	90	100	110	120
Total knee bends	10	18	27	36	45	53	58	62	65	68	70	72

    c. Stefan begins by doing approximately nine knee bends every 10 seconds, but as time goes on the number of knee bends decreases to about two knee bends for every 10 seconds.

    d. Answers will vary. In 25 seconds, he did about 22 or 23 knee bends. In 65 seconds, he did about 55 or 56 knee bends. For 25 seconds, locate the point on the *x*-axis halfway between 20 and 30. Draw a perpendicular line from this point to the graph. Then draw a line from the graph perpendicular to the *y*-axis and read the scale. For 65 seconds, locate the point on the *x*-axis halfway between 60 and 70. Draw a perpendicular line from this point to the graph. Then draw a line from the graph perpendicular to the *y*-axis and read the scale.

2. **a.** Number of breaths and number of meters swum

    b.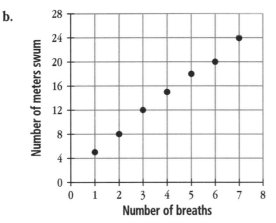

    c. Possible answer: It does not make sense to connect the points because you cannot draw partial breaths.

    d. She made the most progress swimming 5 meters in the first breath. On the table, this shows up as the greatest increase in successive "Number of meters" values. On the graph, this shows up as the greatest "jump" between two points.

    e. Carmen made the least progress between breaths 4 and 5 (2 meters). On the table, this shows up as the smallest increase in successive "Number of meters" values. On the graph, this shows up as the smallest "jump" between two points.

    f. Possible answer: about 14 breaths

Answers to the Quiz

1. **a.**

Weeks	Dominic's money	Norm's money
0	$0	$25
1	10	32
2	20	39
3	30	46
4	40	53
5	50	60
6	60	67
7	70	74
8	80	81
9	90	88
10	100	95

b. Possible graph:

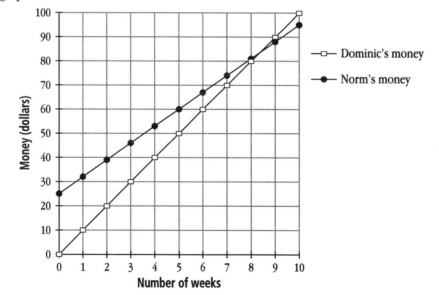

c. Students may write the rule using either words or symbols. In this possible answer, w represents the number of weeks, and s represents the amount saved.

Dominic: Number of weeks times 10 equals total saved, or $10w = s$
Norm: Number of weeks times 7 plus 25 equals the total saved, or $7w + 25 = s$

d. No, not if they put their money in savings at the end of each week. At the end of 8 weeks they will be very close. Dominic will have $80, and Norm will have $81. If they put money in savings at different times during the week, they could have the same amount at various intervals, one of which is between the eighth and the ninth weeks.

e. Dominic will have enough money in 19 weeks. Norm will have enough in 24 weeks.

2. Possible tables:

Time (minutes)	Number of blocks toward theater
0	0
10	4
15	4
20	6
25	4
31	8

Time	Number of blocks toward theater
4:25	0
4:35	4
4:40	4
4:45	6
4:50	4
4:56	8

Possible graph:

Answers to the Question Bank

1. a. Answers will vary.

Time (hours)	Money ($)
1	2.50
2	5.00
3	7.50
4	10.00
5	12.50
6	15.00
7	17.50
8	20.00

b.

Teresa's Earnings

c. Answers will vary. Students may argue for or against connecting the points. As Teresa works longer hours, her money earned increases, indicating a continuous change; but she might occasionally be paid for a full hour although she works only part of an hour, in which case the change would not be continuous.

d. $w = 2.50t$, where t represents the number of hours worked and w represents wages

2. a. Elizabeth makes the most progress at two different times—in the first 25 minutes and from 40 to 45 minutes. This progress is shown on the graph by the steepest inclines.

b. She makes the least progress from 25 to 40 minutes. This is shown by the flattest incline.

3. a. The figures shown are regular polygons; however, students do not have to draw regular polygons to answer the questions.

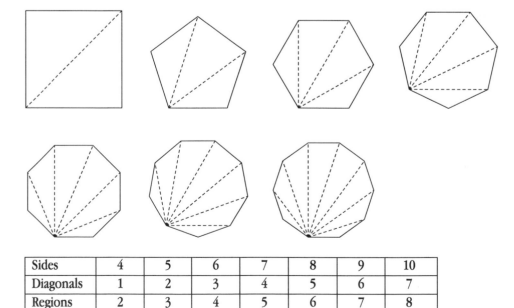

Sides	4	5	6	7	8	9	10
Diagonals	1	2	3	4	5	6	7
Regions	2	3	4	5	6	7	8

   b. $d = n - 3$

   c. See table in part a.

   d. $r = n - 2$

   e. **i.** 18   **ii.** 48   **iii.** 998   **iv.** 999,998

4. **a.** About 380 cartons

   b. About 50 cartons

   c. Between 11:30 and 11:45 and between 12:45 and 1:00

   d. Between noon and 12:15, between 12:30 and 12:45, and between 1:15 and 1:30

   e. The number of milk cartons available during the day decreased rapidly with breaks at noon, 12:30, and 1:15.

   f. Possible answer: The points should not be connected because they cannot sell part of a milk carton.

   g. Answers will vary. Some students might say no because the graph gives a picture of what happened. Others might say yes because it would be helpful to have more specific information especially since the *y*-axis has a fairly large scale.

Answers to the Unit Test

1. **a.** Answers will vary.

Number of shirts	Cost ($)
1	6.95
2	13.90
3	20.85
4	27.80
5	34.75
6	41.70
7	48.65

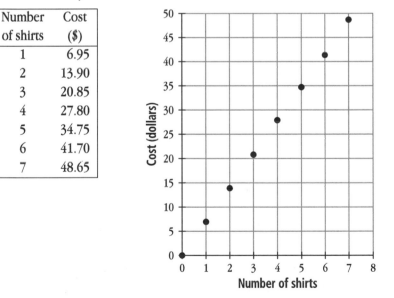

   b. Answers will vary. The points should not be connected because you cannot purchase a portion of a shirt. However, some students may make the point that the cost grows steadily so you could connect the points to see the pattern.

   c. $6.95s = c$, where *s* is the number of shirts and *c* is the cost of the shirts

2. a. Possible table and graph:

Number of CDs	Taylor's Department Store	Buyer's Warehouse
1	$15.49	$37
2	30.98	49
3	46.47	61
4	61.96	73
5	77.45	85
6	92.94	97
7	108.43	109
8	123.92	121
9	139.41	133
10	154.90	145

b. 8 CDs or more

c. Fewer than 8 CDs

d. Answers will vary. Most students will say the table because they can see the actual data, and it is easy to compare the amounts as they look at the numbers increasing. Some will choose the narrative because it helps them think about a rule to fit the situation. Others will choose the graph because it lets them see what is happening, and they can tell which is the better deal by first locating where the lines intersect and then interpreting the graph.

3. Possible answer: Betty pays $8 to rent a bike helmet for every customer on the bike trip. This works when x represents the number of customers and y represents the total cost.

4. a. Answers will vary. The data are probably the same even though they do not look the same because the scales on the graphs are different. If you compare the points or try to write a rule for each one, you get the same information. It does not prove the data are identical, but it does support that assumption.

b. $80n = c$, where n is the number of ounces and c is the calories consumed

5. a. $y = 4x$

b. Possible answer: Rose's Pizza House charges $4.00 per person for an all-you-can-eat pizza buffet. This works when x represents the number of people and y represents the income from Rose's special.

In several schools, Connected Mathematics has been taught to special education students who are part of an inclusion program. In these situations, mathematics and special education staffs work together to find ways to support students who need special help. These teachers have high expectations for all students but know that there are times when adaptations must be made so that special needs students can maximize their opportunities to learn significant mathematics. The suggestions below are given as possible strategies you may want to incorporate in your work with special needs students. The goal with these strategies is to find ways to help students stay engaged with the mathematics of the unit.

Group special education students with regular education students.
We have not found it productive to put all the special education students in a separate group with a special education teacher. Make an effort to place your special education students into groups with helpful, patient regular education students who can explain and share ideas readily. The interaction with the other students appears to have a positive effect on special needs students' learning of mathematics as well as their feelings about themselves and what they can accomplish.

Look ahead for difficulties and be prepared for them.
Some of the problems are very open and challenging. By planning ahead and anticipating difficulties, we have found that we can help keep all of the students involved in mathematics as well as in classroom discussions. Some of the strategies we use include the following:

- Reword some of the more difficult problems in the investigations, follow-up questions, and ACE questions. Below is an adaptation of ACE question 2 from Investigation 1. Key phrases are underlined, and the word *changed* is bolded so that the students pay special attention to these words and phrases. Additional commentary for the students has been added.

  The graph below shows the number of cans of soft drink purchased each hour from a school's vending machine in one day (6 means the time from 5:00 to 6:00, 7 represents the time from 6:00 to 7:00, and so on).

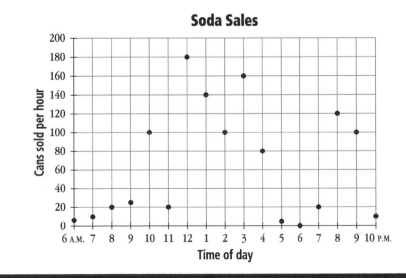

Soda Sales

a. The graph shows the relationship between two variables. <u>What are the variables?</u>

b. Describe how the <u>number of cans sold **changed**</u> during the day. Give an explanation for why these changes might have occurred.

Note:
Look for times when the greatest number of cans are sold.
What times does this happen?
Why would there be a lot of cans sold at that time at a school?
Look for times when there are not many cans sold.
Why would there be only a few cans sold during those times?

- Leave more space between questions for your students to write their answers.

- Break the problem apart. Problems that have several questions embedded in them are often overwhelming to special needs students. Breaking these problems apart and making a list of each question gives these students an opportunity to engage in the problem and use their mathematics to tackle the individual questions needed to do the whole task.

- Work ahead with your special education students. If an upcoming investigation is more complicated than most, have students start to work on it in their "study skills" class before it is introduced in their mathematics class. (Special education students in some middle schools have a daily study skills class with their special education teacher. During this time, the special education teacher works on several subjects with the students.) Working ahead allows special education students more time to think about the problem, sort out the mathematics needed to solve the problem, and prepare for participation in their mathematics class.

Adapt homework assignments.
Homework often takes special education students more time than other students. Adaptation of homework for students is individualized depending on the disabilities of each student. The following suggestions may be helpful.

- Photocopy the homework and allow students to write on the copies. This helps students reduce the time it takes them to do an assignment and to better organize their work. To provide students with more answer space, copy the pages, cut the problems apart, and respace the questions.

- Concentrate on the application and connection problems. If the homework assignment doesn't seem manageable for some special education students, delete the extension problems from their assignments. These problems could be worked on in groups during the "study skills" period or offered as extra credit.

- Create additional practice problems. Choose problems that review the main mathematics skills from the unit. Special education students often need to repeat skills several times before they can make sense of them and incorporate the ideas into their repertoire. These practice problems can be used as a replacement assignment when regular education students are working on extension problems.

In Investigation 4, students find and describe the relationship between distance, rate, and time using words and symbols. Writing rules is often difficult for special needs students. You may need to review the questions and solution strategies for Problems 4.1, 4.2, and 4.3. For additional practice, students could make tables using rates of 45 and 60 miles per hour, then answer questions similar to those in the problems.

Revise the Unit Test, Check-Up, and Quiz.
The following suggestions are possible strategies for working with special needs students. The goal of these strategies is to help students stay engaged with the mathematics of the unit.

- Increase the spacing between problems. Leave room for students to write their answers on the paper, draw pictures or diagrams, and revise their work.

- Increase the size of the print. Students may feel less overwhelmed when there are fewer words in each line.

- Reword problems. Simplify vocabulary where needed.

- Read test questions to students with reading problems. Read one question at a time, coming back to students after they finish each question.

- Highlight or underline important words.

- Replace some of the numbers used in problems with friendlier numbers. For example, in question 1 from the Unit Test, change the cost of the T-shirt from $6.95 to $7.00 to make it easier to determine the scale of the *x*-axis. By using a friendlier number, you can test students on skills other than arithmetic—in this case, the ability to scale a graph.

- Add several questions to make the problem more accessible for your students. For example, you could ask students to make a table before they make a graph, include the beginnings of a table to help students decide what should be in the table and how to organize their work, or add a question that asks your students to write a rule for a situation in words before writing it in symbols.

For example, question 1 from the *Variables and Patterns* Unit Test could be altered as shown on the next page. You may wish to alter other questions on the Unit Test for your special education students using some of the suggestions in this section.

Modified Unit Test

Sidney, Liz, and Malcolm thought it would be a good idea to get a souvenir T-shirt for each customer who went on the Ocean and History Bike Tour. Latisha found a company who would sell them shirts with their logo for $7.00.

a. <u>Make a table</u> that shows how much it costs for T-shirts for different numbers of customers.

Number of customers	T-shirt cost

b. <u>Make a graph</u> of customers and T-shirt costs. Use the information in your table to decide what the scales should be for the two axes.

c. Would it make sense to connect the points on your graph with a line? Why or why not?

d. Write a <u>rule in words</u> that tells how you can find the cost of the T-shirts for any number of customers.

e. Write a <u>rule using symbols</u> that could be used to find the T-shirt cost for any number of customers.

The investigation problems within each unit are intended to be done during class time. Having students share their work in a timely, organized manner has been a challenge for many teachers. Some teachers handle this information and work by giving pairs or groups of students transparency paper for recording and displaying their work. Students can use the overhead projector to share what they have done with the class. One drawback with this method is that only one example can be displayed at a time; transparencies need to be switched back and forth when comparing work done by different groups.

Another strategy teachers have used is giving groups of students large unlined paper, such as 16-by-24-inch newsprint or sheets of grid paper, to record their work. As students finish, the papers are hung at the front of the class for everyone to read, make sense of, and compare to their own work. This method allows all work to be available at all times. It also allows the teacher to know what each group has done with the problem, and to make instructional decisions concerning which student will be called on to report and what ideas to discuss during the summary of the problem. Problem 2.4 (student edition page 24) is a very open problem with an infinite number of solutions. Using large paper and displaying each group's work allows solutions to be easily compared and similarities and differences noticed.

Following are two groups' work for Problem 2.4. These two papers are included to give examples of how students display their work as well as a sampling of what some students have done with this problem. Comments from the teacher follow the student work.

Group A's Display

Group B's Display

Distance in Miles	Time in half hours
0	8:30 A.M.
5	9:00 A.M.
11	9:30 A.M.
21	10:00 A.M.
30	10:30 A.M.
38	11:00 A.M.
41	11:30 A.M.
41	12:00 P.M.
41	12:30 P.M.
45	1:00 P.M.
50	1:30 P.M.
55	2:00 P.M.
60	2:30 P.M.
69	3:00 P.M.
72	3:30 P.M.
80	4:00 P.M.

We decided on our graph by using the notes the Bill and Sarah wrote. We followed each step and figured each distance. To figure out the distance in between we decided on reasonable numbers. Also when they started at 8:30 A.M. to 2:00 P.M. We figured out the data and wrote it down. The same from 2:00 to 3:30 P.m. It said they went the total of 80 miles and went 7.5 hours. that's how we figured out 4:00 p.m.

Teacher's Comments

In my class, I had the students do the questions and the follow-up for Problem 2.4 at the same time. I gave each group of students a large sheet of grid paper for their work. I use grid paper because it makes it quicker for students to record their tables and construct their graphs.

Looking at the given student work, I see that both groups have addressed all three questions, although neither group has done a very good job with the follow-up question. Both explanations are vague, hard to follow, and leave the reader with questions. I am not surprised at this due to the fact that this is the first unit of the new school year. I know it takes time for students to understand the expectations in my class and to get back into the swing of writing and expressing their ideas. Learning to communicate ideas will be a year-long goal for the class.

Further examination of the work suggests that both groups have picked up on the main points from the problem. They show that the travel time was 7.5 hours for the day and that the riders went a total of 80 miles. Both groups also show that the riders stopped for an hour lunch (between 11:30 and 12:30). It appears that group B is having some trouble understanding some of the other changes in rate of travel. They do not show the riders slowing down at 2:00 for a swim or at 3:30 to watch the ships. Group A also seems a bit confused about when the students stopped to watch the ships. By having groups display their work, I did not need to raise these issues; others in the class questioned the groups' table and graph entries.

On the whole, the strategy of using large paper was effective in making all groups accountable and making it easier to compare the different groups' work while using class time efficiently. The displayed work allowed students to compare and contrast how different groups interpreted the story and how their interpretations played out in their tables and graphs. Considerable time was also spent discussing the strategies groups used for creating a reasonable table and how they had to modify their table as they incorporated all the parts of the given report.

Blackline Masters

Labsheet

5.1: Calculator Grids   100

Transparencies

1.1: Problem 1.1   101

1.2A: Problem 1.2   102

1.2B: Grids with Different Scales   103

2.1A: Problem 2.1 Data   104

2.1B: Problem 2.1   105

2.2A: Problem 2.2 Data   106

2.2B: Problem 2.2   107

2.2C: Problem 2.2 Graph   108

2.3: Problem 2.3   109

2.4: Problem 2.4   110

2.5: Problem 2.5   111

3.1A: Bike Rental Fees   112

3.1B: Problem 3.1   113

3.2: Problem 3.2   114

3.3: Problem 3.3   115

3.4A: Problem 3.4   116

3.4B: Sidney's Table   117

4.1A: Problem 4.1 Data   118

4.1B: Problem 4.1   119

4.2A: Problem 4.2 Parts A–C   120

4.2B: Problem 4.2 Parts D–F   121

4.2C: Problem 4.2 Tables   122

4.3A: Problem 4.3 Table   123

4.3B: Problem 4.3   124

5.1: Problem 5.1   125

5.2: Problem 5.2   126

Additional Resources

Family Letter (English)   127

Family Letter (Spanish)   128

Grid Paper   129

Calculator Grids

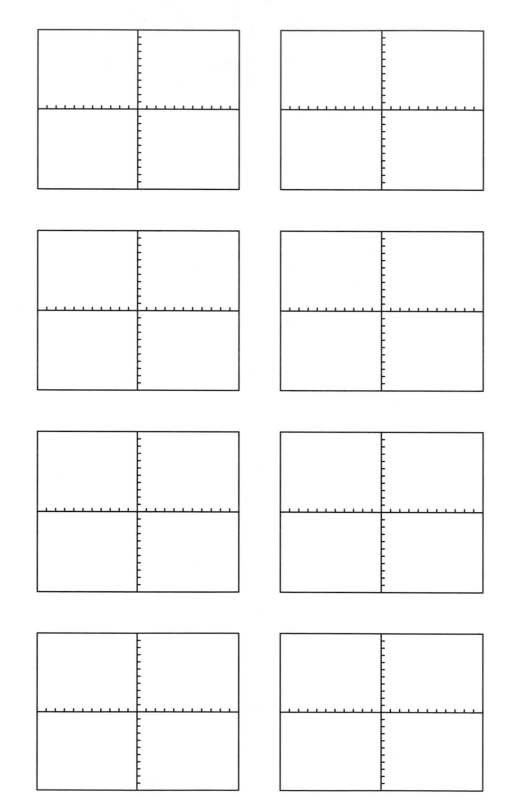

This experiment requires four people:
- a jumper (to do jumping jacks)
- a timer (to keep track of the time)
- a counter (to count jumping jacks)
- a recorder (to write down the number of jumping jacks)

As a group, decide who will do each task.

Prepare a table for recording the total number of jumping jacks after every 10 seconds, up to a total time of 2 minutes (120 seconds).

Time (seconds)	0	10	20	30	40	50	60	70	...
Total number of jumping jacks									

Here's how to do the experiment: When the timer says "go," the jumper begins doing jumping jacks. The counter counts the jumping jacks out loud. Every 10 seconds, the timer says "time" and the recorder records the total number of jumping jacks the jumper has done so far. Repeat the experiment four times so that everyone has a turn at each of the four tasks.

A. Make a graph of your jumping jack data.

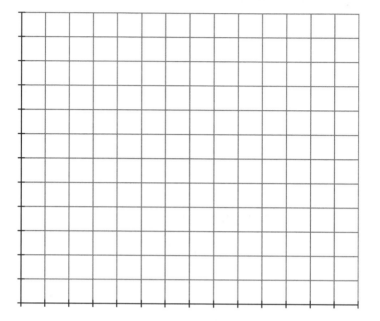

B. What does your graph show about jumping jack rate as time passes? (Another way to say this is, What does your graph show about the *relationship* between the number of jumping jacks and time?)

Jumping Jack Data

Jumping Jack Data

Time (hours)	Distance (miles)
0.0	0
0.5	9
1.0	19
1.5	26
2.0	28
2.5	38
3.0	47
3.5	47
4.0	47
4.5	54
5.0	59
5.5	67
6.0	73
6.5	78
7.0	80
7.5	86
8.0	89

Write a report summarizing the data Tony collected on day 1 of the tour. Describe the distance traveled compared to the time. Look for patterns of change in the data. Be sure to consider the following questions:

- How far did the riders travel in the day? How much time did it take them?

- During which time interval(s) did the riders make the most progress? The least progress?

- Did the riders go further during the first half or the second half of the day's ride?

Time (hours)	Distance (miles)
0.0	0
0.5	8
1.0	15
1.5	19
2.0	25
2.5	27
3.0	34
3.5	40
4.0	40
4.5	40
5.0	45

A. Make a coordinate graph of the (time, distance) data given in the table.

B. Sidney wants to write a report describing day 2 of the tour. Using information from the table or the graph, what could she write about the day's travel? Be sure to consider the following questions:

- How far did the group travel in the day? How much time did it take them?
- During which time interval(s) did the riders make the most progress? The least progress?
- Did the riders go further in the first half or the second half of the day's ride?

C. By analyzing the table, how can you find the time intervals when the riders made the most progress? The least progress? How can you find these intervals by analyzing the graph?

D. Sidney wants to include either the table or the graph in her report. Which do you think she should include? Why?

Atlantic City to Lewes

Day 3 Progress

A. Would it make sense to connect the points on this graph? Explain.

B. Make a table of (time, distance) data from the information in the graph.

C. What do you think happened between hours 2 and 4? Between hours 1.5 and 2?

D. Which method of displaying the (time, distance) data helps you see the changes better, a table or a graph? Explain your choice.

Malcolm and Sarah's Notes

- We started at 8:30 A.M. and rode into a strong wind until our midmorning break.
- About midmorning, the wind shifted to our backs.
- We stopped for lunch at a barbecue stand and rested for about an hour. By this time, we had traveled about halfway to Norfolk.
- At around 2:00 P.M., we stopped for a brief swim in the ocean.
- At around 3:30 P.M., we had reached the north end of the Chesapeake Bay Bridge and Tunnel. We stopped for a few minutes to watch the ships passing by. Since bikes are prohibited on the bridge, the riders put their bikes in the van, and we drove across the bridge.
- We took $7\frac{1}{2}$ hours to complete today's 80-mile trip.

A. Make a table of (time, distance) data that reasonably fits the information in Malcolm and Sarah's notes.

B. Sketch a coordinate graph that shows the same information.

Theo's Speed

A. What was Theo's fastest recorded speed, and when did it occur?

B. What was Theo's slowest recorded speed, and when did it occur?

C. Describe the changes in Theo's speed during the race.

D. The graph only shows Theo's speed at 10-minute intervals; it does not tell us what happened between 10-minute marks. The paths below show five possibilities of how Theo's speed may have changed during the first 10 minutes. Explain in writing what each connecting path would tell about Theo's speed.

Rocky's Cycle Center sent a table of weekly rental fees for various numbers of bikes.

Number of bikes	5	10	15	20	25	30	35	40	45	50
Rental fee	$400	535	655	770	875	975	1070	1140	1180	1200

Adrian's Bike Shop sent a graph of their weekly rental fees. Since the rental fee depends on the number of bikes, they put the number of bikes on the *x*-axis.

Adrian's Bike Shop Fees

A. Which bike shop should Ocean and History Bike Tours use? Explain your choice.

B. Explain how you used the information in the table and the graph to make your decision.

Tour price	Number who would be customers at this price
$150	76
200	74
250	71
300	65
350	59
400	49
450	38
500	26
550	14
600	0

A. If you were to make a graph of the data, which variable would you put on the *x*-axis? Which variable would you put on the *y*-axis? Explain your choices.

B. Make a coordinate graph of the data on grid paper.

C. Based on your graph, what price do you think the tour operators should charge? Explain your reasoning.

© Dale Seymour Publications®

Estimated Tour Profits

A. How much profit will be made if 10 customers go on the tour? 25 customers? 40 customers?

B. How many customers are needed for the partners to earn a $200 profit? A $500 profit? A $600 profit?

C. How does the profit change as the number of customers increases? How is this pattern shown in the graph?

D. If the tour operators reduced their expenses but kept the price at $350, how would this change the graph?

A. Copy Sidney's table. Extend it to give information about income and estimated costs for up to 10 customers.

B. How does the income column change as the number of customers increases? Explain how you can use this relationship to calculate the income for any number of customers.

C. Add and complete a column for "Total cost" (including bike rental, food and camp costs, and van rental) to your table. How does the total cost change as the number of customers increases? Describe how you can calculate the total cost for any number of customers.

D. Add and complete a column for "Profit." What profit would be earned from a trip with 5 customers? 10 customers? 25 customers?

Number of customers	Income	Bike rental	Food and camp costs	Van rental
1	$350	$30	$125	$700
2	700	60	250	700
3				
4				
5				
6				
7				
8				
9				
10				

Time (hours)	Distance (miles)
0	
1	
2	
3	
4	
5	
6	
7	
8	

A. Copy and complete the table and graph to show the relationship between distance and time if the students traveled at a rate of 55 miles per hour.

B. Use your table and graph to estimate the total distance traveled after
   1. 3 hours   **2.** $4\frac{1}{2}$ hours   **3.** $5\frac{1}{4}$ hours

C. If the students continued driving at a steady 55 miles per hour, how far would they go in
   1. 10 hours   **2.** $12\frac{1}{3}$ hours   **3.** 15 hours

D. Look for patterns in the table and graph that help you calculate the distance traveled for any given time. Write a rule, using words, that explains how to calculate the distance traveled for any given time.

E. Use symbols to write your rule from part D as an equation.

A. Make tables of time and distance data, similar to the table you made for Problem 4.1, for travel at 50 miles per hour and 65 miles per hour. Plot the data from both tables on one coordinate grid. Use a different color for each set of data. Using a third color, add data points for the times and distances traveled at 55 miles per hour (from Problem 4.1).

B. How are the tables for the three speeds similar? How are they different?

C. How are the graphs for the three speeds similar? How are they different?

D. 1. Look at the table and graph for 65 miles per hour. What pattern of change in the data helps you calculate the distance for any given time? In words, write a rule that explains how to calculate the distance traveled for any given time.

2. Use symbols to write your rule as an equation.

E. 1. Now write a rule, in words, that explains how to calculate the distance traveled for any given time when the speed is 50 miles per hour.

2. Use symbols to write your rule as an equation.

F. How are the rules for calculating distance for the three speeds similar? How are they different?

At 50 Miles per Hour

Time (hours)	Distance (miles)
0	
1	
2	
3	
4	
5	
6	
7	
8	

At 65 Miles per Hour

Time (hours)	Distance (miles)
0	
1	
2	
3	
4	
5	
6	
7	
8	

Number of customers	Income	Bike rental	Food and camp costs	Van rental	Total cost	Profit
1	$350	$30	$125	$700	$855	-$505
2	700	60	250	700	1010	-310
3	1050	90	375	700	1165	-115
4	1400	120	500	700	1320	80
5	1750	150	625	700	1475	275
6	2100	180	750	700	1630	470
7	2450	210	875	700	1785	665
8	2800	240	1000	700	1940	860
9	3150	270	1125	700	2095	1055
10	3500	300	1250	700	2250	1250

A. Write an equation for the rule to calculate each of the following costs for any number, n, of customers.

    1. bike rental

    2. food and camp costs

    3. van rental

B. Write an equation for the rule to determine the *total cost* for any number, n, of customers.

C. Write an equation for the rule to determine the *profit* for any number, n, of customers.

Experiment with your graphing calculator and the following equations. Graph one set of equations at a time. For each set, two of the graphs will be similar in some way, and one of the graphs will be different. Answer questions A and B for each set.

Set 1: $y = 3x - 4$ $y = x^2$ $y = 3x + 2$
Set 2: $y = 5$ $y = 3x$ $y = 1x$
Set 3: $y = 2x + 3$ $y = 2x - 5$ $y = 0.5x + 2$
Set 4: $y = 2x$ $y = 2 \div x$ $y = x + 5$

A. 1. Which two equations in the set have graphs that are similar?

2. In what ways are the two graphs similar?

3. In what ways are the equations for the two graphs similar?

B. 1. Which equation in the set has a graph that is different from the graphs of the other equations?

2. In what way is the graph different from the other graphs?

3. In what way is the equation different from the other equations?

A. 1. Use your calculator to make a table for the equation $y = 3x$.

2. Copy part of the calculator's table onto your paper.

3. Use your table to find y if $x = 5$.

B. 1. Use your calculator to make a table for the equation $y = 0.5x + 2$.

2. Copy part of the calculator's table onto your paper.

3. Use your table to find y if $x = 5$.

Dear Family,

The first unit in your child's course of study in mathematics class this year is *Variables and Patterns*. Students are introduced to algebraic concepts as they explore situations that change, such as how many miles are covered over several hours of a bicycle trip, and how profit earned in running a bicycle company is related to changes in income or expenses.

This unit's focus is on ways to describe situations that change. Students write descriptions about events. They record data in tables, make graphs to show changes that are occurring, use words to describe the patterns of change, and compare these forms of representation. By the end of this unit, students will be able to use variables in writing simple rules, or equations, to describe patterns they observe in the changing situations.

As part of this unit, students use graphing calculators to make tables and graphs. Students enter equations into the graphing calculators, and a graph of the data on a coordinate grid is displayed. The use of a graphing calculator helps students explore many more situations than would be possible if the work is done by hand. This allows students to interpret and compare more data sets.

You can help your child in several ways:

- Invite your child to describe the jumping jacks experiment and to keep you informed about the events that happen in the situation involving bicycle tours.

- Encourage your child to do his or her homework every day. Look over the homework and make sure all questions are answered and that explanations are clear.

- Have your child share his or her mathematics notebook with you, showing you the tables and graphs he or she has constructed and what has been recorded about patterns and variables. Ask your child to explain why these ideas are important.

As always, if you have any questions or concerns about this unit or your child's progress in the class, please feel free to call. We are interested in your child and want to be sure that this year's mathematics experiences are enjoyable and promote a firm understanding of mathematics.

Sincerely,

Estimada familia,

La primera unidad del programa de matemáticas de su hijo o hija para este curso se llama *Variables and Patterns* (Variables y patrones). Los alumnos aprenderán conceptos algebraicos al explorar situaciones cambiantes como, por ejemplo, las siguientes: ¿Cuántas millas se recorren durante una excursión en bicicleta de varias horas? y ¿Cómo están relacionadas las ganancias de una compañía de bicicletas con los cambios en los ingresos o en los gastos?

Esta unidad trata principalmente sobre las diferentes maneras de describir situaciones cambiantes. Los alumnos harán descripciones por escrito sobre sucesos, anotarán datos en tablas, harán gráficas que muestren los cambios producidos, utilizarán palabras para describir los patrones de variación y compararán las diversas formas de representación. Una vez finalizada la unidad, serán capaces de emplear variables en la formulación de sencillas reglas o ecuaciones a fin de describir patrones que observen en situaciones cambiantes.

Como parte de esta unidad, los alumnos utilizarán calculadoras de gráficas para hacer tablas y gráficas. En ellas introducirán ecuaciones para que a continuación aparezca en la cuadrícula de coordenadas la gráfica de los datos. El uso de este tipo de calculadoras ayuda a los alumnos a explorar muchas más situaciones de las que sería posible si el trabajo fuera realizado a mano. Además, esto les permite interpretar y comparar un mayor número de conjuntos de datos.

Para ayudar a su hijo o hija, ustedes pueden hacer lo siguiente:

- Pídanle que describa el experimento de los títeres y que les tenga al día acerca de los sucesos que ocurran en la situación de las excursiones en bicicleta.

- Anímenle a hacer la tarea todos los días. Repásenla para asegurarse de que conteste todas las preguntas y escriba con claridad las explicaciones.

- Pídanle que comparta con ustedes su cuaderno de matemáticas, que les enseñe tanto las tablas y las gráficas que ha construido como las anotaciones sobre los patrones y las variables. Díganle que les explique la importancia de dichas anotaciones.

Y como de costumbre, si ustedes necesitan más detalles o aclaraciones respecto a esta unidad o sobre los progresos de su hijo o hija en esta clase, no duden en llamarnos. Nos interesa su hijo o hija y queremos asegurarnos de que las experiencias matemáticas que tenga este año sean lo más amenas posibles y ayuden a fomentar en él o ella una sólida comprensión de las matemáticas.

Atentamente,

Additional Practice

Investigation 1	132
Investigation 2	134
Investigation 3	136
Investigation 4	138
Investigation 5	139
Answer Keys	140

Investigation 1

Use these problems for additional practice after Investigation 1.

1. The convenience store across the street from Metropolis School has been keeping track of their popcorn sales. The table below shows the total number of bags sold beginning at 6:00 A.M. on a particular day.

   a. Complete the third column to show the number of bags of popcorn sold during *each* hour. For example, 3 bags were sold between 6:00 A.M. and 7:00 A.M., 12 bags (15 – 3) were sold between 7:00 A.M. and 8 A.M., and so on.

   b. Make a coordinate graph of these data. Which variable did you put on the *x*-axis? Why?

   c. What were the most popular times for buying popcorn? Explain your reasoning.

   d. What is the mean number of bags sold per hour? Note that since there is no "Bags sold per hour" value for 6:00 A.M., you are finding the mean of only 13 values.

   e. What is the median number of bags sold per hour?

   f. How do your answers for parts d and e compare? Why do you think this is so?

Time	Total bags sold	Bags sold per hour
6:00 A.M.	0	—
7:00 A.M.	3	3
8:00 A.M.	15	12
9:00 A.M.	20	5
10:00 A.M.	26	
11:00 A.M.	30	
noon	45	
1:00 P.M.	58	
2:00 P.M.	58	
3:00 P.M.	62	
4:00 P.M.	74	
5:00 P.M.	83	
6:00 P.M.	88	
7:00 P.M.	92	

2. The graph on the next page shows the number of cans of soft drink purchased each hour from a school's vending machines in one day (5 means the time from 4:00 to 5:00, 6 represents the time from 5:00 to 6:00, and so on).

   a. Make a table that shows time of day and the *total* number of cans of soda sold up to that time. For example, at 6:00 A.M. about 6 cans had been sold. By 7:00 A.M., about 10 more cans had been sold, for a total of 16 cans.

   b. Make a coordinate graph of the data in your table. Which variable did you put on the *x*-axis? Why?

   c. On the day represented in the graph, what were the most popular times for buying soda? Explain your reasoning.

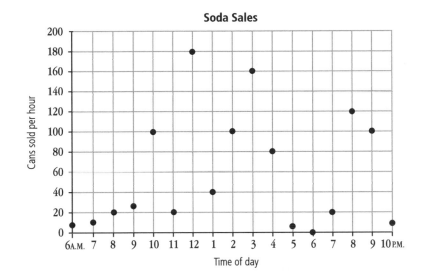

3. The graph below shows the number of cans of food collected by Mr. Darrow's students on each of the five days of the school's holiday food drive.

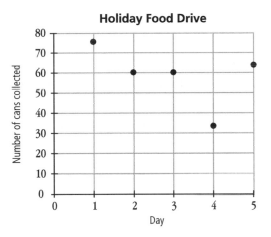

a. The graph shows the relationship between two variables. What are the variables?

b. On which day were the most cans of food collected? How many cans were collected on that day?

c. What total number of cans were collected over the 5 days? Explain your reasoning.

d. What is the mean number of cans collected over the five days? Explain your reasoning.

c. On this graph, does it make sense to connect the points with line segments? Explain your reasoning.

Investigation 2

Use these problems for additional practice after Investigation 2.

1. The *Metropolis City Herald* included the graph below in a story about the amount of city land used for trash between 1990 and 1995.

Landfill Area Used 1990–1995

a. The graph shows the relationship between two variables. What are they?

b. What is the difference between the least and greatest amount of land used for trash?

c. Between which two years did the area used for trash stay the same?

d. On this graph, what information is given by the lines connecting the points? Is this information necessarily accurate? Explain your reasoning.

e. In 1990, the total area available for trash was 120 square kilometers. Make a coordinate graph that shows the landfill area remaining in each year from 1990 to 1995.

2. Below is a chart of the water depth in a harbor during a typical 24-hour day. The water level rises and falls with the tide.

Hours since midnight	0	1	2	3	4	5	6	7	8	9	10	11	12
Depth (meters)	8.4	8.9	9.9	10.7	11.2	12.1	12.9	12.2	11.3	10.6	9.4	8.3	8.0

Hours since midnight	13	14	15	16	17	18	19	20	21	22	23	24
Depth (meters)	8.4	9.4	10.8	11.4	12.2	13.0	12.4	11.3	10.4	9.8	8.6	8.1

a. Make a coordinate graph of the data.

b. During which time interval(s) does the depth of the water increase the most?

  c. During which time interval(s) does the depth of the water decrease the most?

  d. Would it make sense to connect the points on the graph? Why or why not?

  e. Is it easier to use the table or the graph to answer parts b and c?

3. Make a table and a graph of (time, temperature) data that fit the following information about a day on the road:

  • We started riding at 9:00 A.M. once the fog had burned off. The day was quite cool. The temperature was 52°F, and the sun was shining brightly.

  • About midmorning, the temperature rose to 70°F and cloud cover moved in, which kept the temperature steady until lunch time.

  • Suddenly the sun burst through the clouds, and the temperature began to climb. By late afternoon, it was 80°F.

4. The three graphs below show the progress of a cyclist at different times during a ride. For each graph, describe the rider's progress over the time interval.

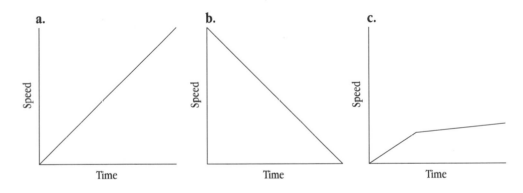

5. Make a graph that shows your hunger level over the course of a day. Label the *x*-axis from 6 A.M. to midnight. Write a story about what happened during the day in relation to your hunger level.

Investigation 3

Use these problems for additional practice after Investigation 3.

1. This table shows the fees charged for roller blading at a roller rink.

Number of minutes	30	60	90	120	150	180
Cost (dollars)	3.50	7.00	10.50	14.00	17.50	21.00

    a. Make a coordinate graph of these data.

    b. Would it make sense to connect the points on your graph? Why or why not?

    c. Using the table, describe the pattern of change in the total skating fee as the number of minutes increases. How is this pattern shown in the graph?

2. A roller-blade supply store rents roller blades for $2.50 per skater.

    a. Using increments of 5 skaters, make a table showing the total rental charge for 0 to 50 skaters. Make a coordinate graph of these data.

    b. Compare the pattern of change in your table and graph with the patterns you found in the skating fees in question 1. Describe any similarities and differences between the two sets of data.

3. The coordinate graph below shows the total monthly sales for the concession stand at the roller rink.

    a. Use the graph to make a table of data showing the sales for each month.

    b. The profit made by the concession stand is half of the sales. Make a table of data that shows the profit made by the concession stand for each month.

    c. Make a coordinate graph of the data from part b. Use the same scale used in the sales graph above. Describe how the sales graph and the profit graph are similar and how they are different.

4. During the 5-day bike trip, Celia kept track of how much money she spent on food each day, rounding up to the nearest dollar. She recorded the data as coordinate pairs: (1, 14), (2, 11), (3, 15), (4, 10), (5, 13). The *x*-coordinate in each pair represents the day of the trip, and the *y*-coordinate represents the money Celia spent on food. For example, (3, 15) means that on the third day of the trip, Celia spend $15.

    a. What is the total amount Celia spent on food for the trip?

    b. Between which two days did Celia's food spending increase the most? Between which two days did Celia's food spending decrease the most?

    c. What is the mean of Celia's food costs for the five-day trip?

Investigation 4

Use these problems for additional practice after Investigation 4.

1. The equation $d = 44t$ represents the distance, in miles, covered after traveling 44 miles per hour for t hours.

    a. Make a table that shows the distance traveled, according to this equation, for every half hour between 0 hours and 4 hours.

    b. Sketch a graph that shows the distance traveled between 0 and 4 hours.

    c. If $t = 2.5$, what is d?

    d. If $d = 66$, what is t?

    e. Does it make sense to connect the points on this graph with line segments? Why or why not?

In 2–6, use symbols to express the rule as an equation. Use single letters to stand for the variables. Identify what each letter represents.

2. The perimeter of a rectangle is twice its length plus twice its width.

3. The area of a triangle is one-half its base multiplied by its height.

4. Three big marshmallows are needed to make each s'more.

5. The number of quarters in an amount of money expressed in dollars is four times the number of dollars.

6. A half cup of unpopped popcorn is needed to make 6 cups of popped popcorn.

7. The number of students at Metropolis Middle School is 21 multiplied by the number of teachers.

    a. Use symbols to express the rule relating the number of students and the number of teachers as an equation. Use single letters for your variables, and explain what each letter represents.

    b. If there are 50 teachers at Metropolis Middle School, how many students attend the school?

    c. If 1260 students attend Metropolis Middle School, how many teachers teach at the school?

8. The table below shows the relationship between the side length and the area of squares.

Side length	Area
1	1
1.5	2.25
2	4
2.5	6.25
3	9
.	.
.	.
.	.

    a. Use symbols to express the rule relating the side length of a square to its area as an equation. Use single letters for your variables, and explain what each letter represents.

    b. Use your equation to find the area of a square with a side length of 6 centimeters.

    c. Use your equation to find the side length of a square with an area of 1.44 square centimeters.

Investigation 5

Use these problems for additional practice after Investigation 5.

1. In a–c, sets of (x, y) coordinates are given. For each set, find a pattern in the data, and express the rule for the pattern as an equation.

    a. $(0, 0)$, $(1, 0.5)$, $(2, 1)$, $(3, 1.5)$, $(6, 3)$, $(10, 5)$, $(21, 10.5)$, $(1000, 500)$

    b. $(1, 2)$, $(2, 5)$, $(3, 8)$, $(4, 11)$, $(5, 14)$, $(10, 29)$, $(100, 299)$

    c. $(0, 4)$, $(1, 5)$, $(2, 8)$, $(3, 13)$, $(4, 20)$, $(5, 29)$, $(6, 40)$, $(7, 53)$, $(10, 104)$

2. Enter each of the equations from question 1 into your graphing calculator. Describe the graph of each equation. How do the three graphs compare?

3. Graph the equations $y = 2x - 1$ and $y = x$ in the same window of your graphing calculator.

    a. Do the graphs of the two equations cross? If they do, give the (x, y) coordinates of the point(s) where the graphs cross.

    b. Do you think it's possible for two different lines to cross at more than one point?

    c. Use your graphing calculator to help you find two equations whose graphs do not cross.

Investigation 1

1. **a.**

Time	Total bags sold	Bags sold per hour
6:00 A.M.	0	—
7:00 A.M.	3	3
8:00 A.M.	15	12
9:00 A.M.	20	5
10:00 A.M.	26	6
11:00 A.M.	30	4
noon	45	15
1:00 P.M.	58	13
2:00 P.M.	58	0
3:00 P.M.	62	4
4:00 P.M.	74	12
5:00 P.M.	83	9
6:00 P.M.	88	5
7:00 P.M.	92	4

b. Time is on the x-axis because the number of bags sold depends on the time.

Bags of Popcorn Sold Each Hour

c. between 7 A.M. and 8 A.M., between 11 A.M. and 1 P.M., and between 3 P.M. and 4 P.M.; these are the times when the numbers of bags sold per hour are the greatest.

d. about 7.1 bags

e. 5 bags

f. The mean is greater than median because the greater values such as 12, 13, and 15 pull the mean up.

2. **a.** Students tables will vary slightly since the numbers are estimated from the graph.

Time	Total cans sold
6:00 A.M.	6
7:00 A.M.	16
8:00 A.M.	36
9:00 A.M.	61
10:00 A.M.	161
11:00 A.M.	181
noon	361
1:00 P.M.	401
2:00 P.M.	501
3:00 P.M.	661
4:00 P.M.	741
5:00 P.M.	746
6:00 P.M.	746
7:00 P.M.	766
8:00 P.M.	886
9:00 P.M.	986
10:00 P.M.	996

b. Time is on the *x*-axis because the number of cans sold depends on the time.

c. Between 11 A.M. and noon, between 2 P.M. and 3 P.M., and between 7 P.M. and 8 P.M. These intervals show the greatest change in the number of sodas sold.

3. **a.** day of the food drive and cans collected

    b. day 1; about 75 cans

    c. Add the cans collected each day to find the total: $76 + 60 + 60 + 33 + 63 = 292$ cans.

    d. Divide the total number of cans collected by the number of days: $\frac{292}{5} = 58.4$ cans.

    e. no; Connecting points would suggest that cans could be collected between days.

Investigation 2

1. **a.** year and land area in square kilometers

    b. about 16 square kilometers

    c. between 1990 and 1991 and between 1993 and 1994

    d. Possible answer: The information shows a constant change in the area used for landfill from one year to the next. It isn't necessarily accurate because we do not know the details of how the landfill "grew" from one year to the next.

    e.

Landfill Area Remaining 1990–1995

2. a.

Harbor Water Depth

b. From 14 hours after midnight to 15 hours after midnight, the depth increases by the greatest amount, 1.4 meters.

c. Between 9 and 10 hours after midnight and between 22 and 23 hours after midnight, the depth decreases by the greatest amount, 1.2 meters.

d. It makes sense to connect the points because the depth is changing continuously.

e. Possible answer: It is easier to use the table because you can read the exact values.

3. Answers will vary.

4. a. The graph shows the cyclist's speed constantly increasing.

b. The graph shows the cyclist's speed constantly decreasing.

c. The graph shows the cyclist's speed increasing and then leveling off.

5. Answers will vary.

Investigation 3

1. a.

Roller Blading Costs

b. Possible answer: It would make sense to connect the points on the graph if there are partial fees for minutes between half hours.

c. The cost increases by $3.50 for each additional half hour of skating. On the graph, this is shown by a straight line pattern going up as we read from left to right. The values on the "Cost" axis increase by $3.50 for each increase of 30 on the "Minutes" axis.

2. a.

Number of skaters	0	5	10	15	20	25	30	35	40	45	50
Rental charge (dollars)	0	12.50	25	37.50	50	62.50	75	87.50	100	112.50	125

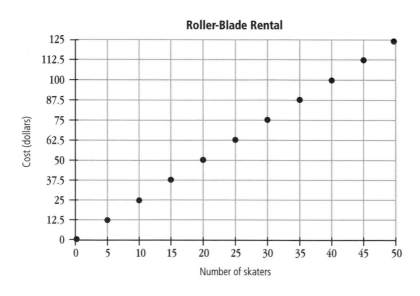

Roller-Blade Rental

b. Possible answer: Both tables show a constant increase in the *y*-values as the *x*-values increase by a fixed amount. The points on both graphs follow a straight-line pattern.

3. a.

Month	Sales
Sept.	$100
Oct.	$75
Nov.	$150
Dec.	$200
Jan.	$150
Feb.	$200
Mar.	$100
Apr.	$125
May	$100

b.

Month	Profit
Sept.	$50
Oct.	$37.50
Nov.	$75
Dec.	$100
Jan.	$75
Feb.	$100
Mar.	$50
Apr.	$62.50
May	$50

c. The graph of the profit is similar to the sales graph except that each *y*-coordinate in the profit graph is exactly half the value of the *y*-coordinate in the total sales graph.

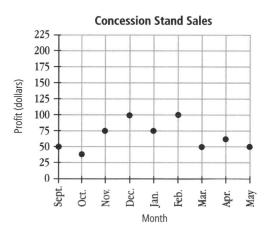

Concession Stand Sales

4. **a.** The sum of the *y*-coordinates is 63. So Celia spent $63 on food over the five days.

    b. Celia's greatest increase in spending was $4 from the second day to the third day. The greatest decrease, $5, came between the third day and the fourth day.

    c. Celia spent an average of $\frac{63}{5} = \$12.60$ on food each day.

Investigation 4

1. **a.**

Time (hours)	0	0.5	1.0	1.5	2.0	2.5	3.0	3.5	4.0
Distance (miles)	0	22	44	66	88	110	132	154	176

    b.

Traveling at 44 Miles per Hour

    c. $d = 110$

    d. $t = 1.5$

    e. It makes sense to connect points because the distance increases at a constant rate.

2. *p* is perimeter, *l* is length, *w* is width: $p = 2l + 2w$

3. *A* is area, *b* is base, *h* is height: $A = \frac{1}{2} \times b \times h$

4. *s* is number of s'mores, *m* is number of marshmallows: $s = 3 \times m$

5. *q* is the number of quarters, *D* is the amount of money in dollars: $q = 4 \times D$

6. *u* is cups of unpopped popcorn, *p* is cups of popped popcorn: $p = 12u$

7. **a.** S is number of students, T is number of teachers: $S = 21 \times T$

   b. $S = 21 \times 50 = 1050$ students

   c. If $1260 = 21 \times T$, what number must 21 be multiplied by to get a product of 1260? $T = 60$ teachers.

8. **a.** A is the area, s is the side length: $A = s \times s$ or $A = s^2$

   b. $A = 36$ cm^2

   c. 1.44 cm$^2 = s \times s$, and so $s = 1.2$ cm

Investigation 5

1. **a.** $y = 0.5x$

   b. $y = 3x - 1$

   c. $y = x^2 + 4$

2. The graphs of $y = 3x - 1$ and $y = 0.5x$ are both lines that rise from left to right. The graph of $y = x^2 + 4$ is U-shaped.

3. **a.** The graphs cross at (1, 1).

   b. No, two lines are either parallel, or they have exactly one point of intersection.

   c. Possible answer: $y = 3x + 1$ and $y = 3x + 4$

change To become different. For example, temperatures rise and fall, and prices increase and decrease. In mathematics, quantities that change are called *variables*.

coordinate graph A graphical representation of pairs of related numerical values that shows the relationship between two variables. It relates the independent variable (*x*-axis) and the dependent variable (*y*-axis).

coordinate pair An ordered pair of numbers used to locate a point on a coordinate grid. The first number in a coordinate pair is the value for the *x*-coordinate, and the second number is the value for the *y*-coordinate.

dependent variable One of the two variables in a relationship. Its value depends upon or is determined by the other variable, called the *independent variable*. For example, the cost of a long-distance phone call (dependent variable) depends on how long you talk (independent variable).

distance/time/rate of speed The relationship of these terms can be defined as: distance d is determined by multiplying the rate r by the time t, or $d = rt$. For example, if you drive a car 55 miles per hour (rate) for 3 hours (time), you will travel 165 miles (distance).

equation, formula A rule containing variables that represents a mathematical relationship. An example is the formula for finding the area of a circle: $A = \pi r^2$.

income/cost/profit The relationship of these terms can be defined as: profit p is what is left when cost c is subtracted from income i, or $p = i - c$. For example, if you can make a hot dog for 25 cents (cost) and sell it for 29 cents (income), you earn 4 cents (profit).

independent variable One of the two variables in a relationship. Its value determines the value of the other variable, called the *dependent variable*. If you organize a bike tour, for example, the number of people who register to go (independent variable) determines the cost for renting bikes (dependent variable).

pattern A change that occurs in a predictable way. For example, the colored squares on a checkerboard form this pattern: the colors of the squares alternate. The sequence of square numbers: 1, 4, 9, 16 . . . form this pattern: the numbers increase by the next odd number.

range of values Those values for the variables that make sense for the data being considered. You use the range when you ask yourself these questions before making a graph of a set of data: *What are the values of the data that will fit on the graph? What scale must I choose for the graph so that all of the data will fit?*

relationship An association between two or more variables. If one of the variables changes, the other variable may also change, and the change may be predictable.

rule A summary of a predictable relationship that tells how to find the value of a variable. It is a pattern that is consistent enough to be written down, made into an equation, graphed, or made into a table. For example, this rule relates time, rate, and distance: distance is equal to rate times time, or $d = rt$.

scale A labeling scheme used on the axes on a coordinate grid.

symbolic form Anything written or expressed through the use of symbols. In mathematics, for example, letters and numbers are often used to represent a rule rather than words.

table A list of values for two or more variables that shows the relationship between them. Tables often contain data from observations, experiments, or a series of arithmetic operations. A table may show a pattern of change between two variables that can be used to predict values for other entries in the table.

variable A quantity that can change. Letters are often used as symbols to represent variables in rules or equations that describe patterns.

x-**axis** The number line that is horizontal on a coordinate grid.

y-**axis** The number line that is vertical on a coordinate grid.

cambiar Variar, volverse diferente. Por ejemplo, las temperaturas suben y bajan, los precios aumentan y se reducen, y así sucesivamente. En matemática, las cantidades que cambian se llaman *variables*.

ecuación, fórmula Una regla que contiene variables que representa una relación matemática. Un ejemplo de ello es la fórmula para hallar el área de un círculo: $A = \pi r^2$.

eje de las x La línea numérica horizontal en una cuadrícula de coordenadas.

eje de las y La línea numérica vertical en una cuadrícula de coordenadas.

escala Un esquema de rotulación empleado en los ejes de una cuadrícula de coordenadas.

forma simbólica Algo escrito o expresado mediante el uso de símbolos. Por ejemplo, muchas veces se usan letras y números en lugar de palabras para representar reglas matemáticas.

gráfica de coordenadas Una representación gráfica de pares de valores numéricos asociados que muestra la relación existente entre dos variables. Dicha representación relaciona la variable independiente (mostrada en el eje de las x) y la variable dependiente (mostrada en el eje de las y).

par de coordenadas Un par ordenado de números utilizado para localizar un punto en una cuadrícula de coordenadas. El primer número del par de coordenadas es el valor de la coordenada x y el segundo número es el valor de la coordenada y.

patrón Una variación que ocurre de manera predecible. Por ejemplo, los cuadrados del tablero de damas forman un patrón en el que los colores de los cuadrados se alternan. La secuencia de números cuadrados: 1, 4, 9, 16, ... forma un patrón en el que los números aumentan según la cifra del siguiente número impar. Es decir, 4 es 3 más que 1, 9 es 5 más que 4, 16 es 7 más que 9, y así sucesivamente.

regla Un resumen de una relación predecible que indica cómo hallar el valor de una variable. Se trata de un patrón que, debido a su coherencia, puede escribirse, convertirse en una ecuación, representarse gráficamente o utilizarse para hacer una tabla. Por ejemplo, la siguiente regla relaciona tiempo, velocidad y distancia: la distancia es igual al producto de la velocidad y el tiempo, o sea $d = rt$.

relación Una asociación entre dos o más variables. Si una de las variables cambia, la otra variable también puede cambiar, y dicho cambio puede ser predecible.

tabla Una lista de valores para dos o más variables que muestra la relación existente entre ellas. Frecuentemente, las tablas contienen datos provenientes de observaciones, experimentos o de una serie de operaciones aritméticas. Una tabla puede mostrar un patrón de variación existente entre dos variables, el cual puede utilizarse para predecir los valores de otras entradas de la tabla.

variable Una cantidad que puede cambiar. Suelen usarse letras como símbolos para representar las variables de las reglas o ecuaciones que describen patrones.

variable dependiente Una de las dos variables en una relación. Su valor depende del valor de la otra variable llamada variable independiente, o está determinado por dicho valor. Por ejemplo, el costo de una llamada telefónica de larga distancia (variable dependiente) depende de la duración de la conversación (variable independiente).

variable independiente Una de las dos variables relacionadas. Su valor determina el de la otra variable, llamada variable dependiente. Por ejemplo, si organizas un recorrido en bicicleta, el número de personas inscritas (variable independiente) determina el costo del alquiler de las bicicletas (variable dependiente).

Index

Algebra, 1a, 3
  variable relationships and, 49
Assateague Island, 22
Assessment Resources
  1k, 4a, 84
  ACE Assignments, 1k
  Check-Up, 1k, 70–72, 85
  Embedded Assessment, 1k
  Notebook Checklist, 1k–1l, 83
  Notebook/Journal, 1k–1l
  pacing chart, 1j
  Partner Quiz, 1k
  Question Bank, 1k, 76–78, 87–89
  Quiz, 73–76, 86–87
  Recording and Displaying Student Work, 95–97
  revising for special needs, 93–94
  Supporting Inclusion Students, 91–94
  Unit Test, 1l, 79–82, 89–90
Assessment Summary, 1k–1l
Axes, on a coordinate graph, 7–8

Change
  ACE, 26–34, 42–47
  analyzing, 1a
  graphing, 17f, 18–25, 35a–35f, 36–41, 48a–48f
  recording on a table, 1b–1c, 17f, 18–25, 35a–35f, 36–41, 48a–48f
  verbal description of, 1b, 17f, 18–25, 35a–35f, 36–41, 48a–48f
Continuous relationship, 1d, 18–25, 35a–35f, 36–41
Coordinate graph
  ACE, 10–17, 26–34, 42–47
  making, 7–9, 17b–17d
  to show change, 18–25, 35a–35f, 36–41, 48a–48f
Coordinate pair, 21
Coordinate point, plotting, 9

Data
  ACE, 10–17, 26–34, 42–47
  experimental, 6–9, 17a–17d
  on a graph, 4, 7–16, 17b–17d, 17f, 18–25, 35a–35f, 36–41, 48a–48f

on a table, 4, 17a–17d, 17f, 18–25, 35a–35f, 36–41, 48a–48f
  verbal description of, 4, 17f, 18–25, 35a–35f, 36–41, 48a–48f
Dependent variable, 8
Diagram Code technique, 17, 48, 68
Discrete relationship, 1d, 18–25, 35a–35f, 36–41

Enactment technique, 19
Equation, 49, 12 *See also* **Formula**
  ACE, 54–59, 64–67
  for cost, 52–53, 60d–60e
  for distance, 50–51, 60a–60d
  graphing, 60j, 61–63, 68a–68d
  for income, 52, 60d–60e
  for profit, 52–53, 60d–60e
  for a rule, 48n, 49–53, 60a–60e
  for speed, 51–52, 60c–60d
  table for, 63
  table of variables for, 4, 48n, 49–53, 60a–60e
  to describe a pattern, 4, 48n, 49–53, 60a–60e
  to relate variables, 48n, 49–53, 60a–60e
  writing, 48n, 49–53, 60c–60e
Experiment, jumping jack, 6–9
Exponential relation, 1b

Family Letter
  English, 127
  Spanish, 128
Formula, 49, 12 *See also* **Equation**
  ACE, 54–59
  circumference of a circle, 49–50
  rules and, 49–53

Graph
  ACE, 10–17, 26–34, 42–47, 54–59, 64–67
  from an equation, 60j, 61–63, 63a–63d
  coordinate, 7–9, 17b–17d
  for recording change, 1c–1d, 17b–17d, 17f, 18–25, 35a–35f, 36–41, 48a–48f
  linear, 1c–1d
  on a graphing calculator, 60j, 61–63, 63b–63c

Index

predicting from, 36–40
rules and, 48n, 49–53, 60a–60e
selecting a scale for, 1e, 8, 17b–17d, 35b, 35d
Graphing calculator, ACE, 64–67
classroom management, 1h–1i
graphing on, 1f, 4, 60j, 61–63, 68b–68c
making tables on, 1f, 4, 63, 68c–68d
setup notes, 68a–68b

Inclusion student, support, 91–93
Income, 39, 48a
Independent variable, 8
Investigation, 4a
Analyzing Graphs and Tables, 35i, 36–48, 48a–48m
Graphing Change, 17f, 18–35, 35a–35k
Patterns and Rules, 48n, 49–60, 60a–60i
summary of, 1g
Using a Graphing Calculator, 60j, 61–68, 68a–68e
Variables and Coordinate Graphs, 4b, 5–17, 17a–17e

Journal, 17, 35, 48, 60, 68, 68f

Linear graph, 1c–1d, 48e, 48n
Linear relation, 1b, 1c–1d, 48e, 48n, 60a
Logo, drawing regular polygons with, 47
Looking Back and Looking Ahead:
  Unit Reflections, 68f–h

Materials list, complete, 1h
for Investigation 1, 4b
for Investigation 2, 17f
for Investigation 3, 35f
for Investigation 4, 48n
for Investigation 5, 60j
Mathematical content, 1b–1e
Mathematical goals, 1f
Analyzing Graphs and Tables, 35f
Graphing Change, 17f
Patterns and Rules, 48n
Using a Graphing Calculator, 60j
Variables and Coordinate Graphs, 4b

Mathematical Highlights, 4
Mathematical Reflections, 17, 35, 48, 60, 68

Nonlinear relationship, 60i
Notebook Checklist, 1k–1l, 83

Original Rebus technique, 35, 60
Overview, 1a

Pacing chart, 1j
Pattern, 7
ACE, 42–47, 54–59
additive, 1b
of change, 1b–1c
multiplicative, 1b
predicting from, 1f, 7, 38, 41
rules and, 48n, 49–53, 60a–60e
Polygon, drawing regular, 47
Prediction
from a graph, 4, 36–40
from a pattern, 7, 38, 41
from a table, 40–41
using rules, 49–53
Problem-solving goals, 1f
Analyzing Graphs and Tables, 35f
Graphing Change, 17f
Patterns and Rules, 48n
Using a Graphing Calculator, 60j
Variables and Coordinate Graphs, 4b
Profit, 48a

Range of values, 8
Rebus Scenario technique, 5
Relationship, 9, 17d
ACE, 26–34, 42–47, 54–59
continuous, 1d, 18–25, 36–41
discrete, 1d, 18–25, 36–41
graphic description of, 1c–1e, 17f, 18–25, 35a–35f, 36–41, 48a–48f
money and number, 36–41, 52–53
nonlinear, 60i
time and distance, 18–24, 35d–35e, 50–51

Index

time and speed, 24–25, 35e–35f, 51–52
verbal description of, 1b, 17f, 18–25, 35a–35f, 36–41, 48a–48f
Resources, for teachers, 1i
Rule
  ACE, 54–59
  equation for, 48n, 49–53, 60a–60e
  pattern and, 48n, 49–53, 60a–60e

Scale, 8
  selecting, 1e, 1f, 8, 35b, 35d
Special education student, support, 91–93
Symbolic form, 49

Table, 6
  ACE, 10–17, 26–34, 42–47, 54–59, 64–67
  from an equation, 63
  on a graphing calculator, 60j, 63, 63c–63d
  to organize data, 1b–1c, 1f, 6–9
  predicting from, 40–41
  recording change on, 17f, 18–25, 35a–35f, 36–41, 48a–48f
  rules and, 48n, 49–53, 60a–60e

Technology, 1h–1i
Turtle Math, drawing regular polygons, 47

Variable, 1f, 3, 7
  ACE, 10–17, 42–47, 54–59
  dependent, 8
  expressing relationships with, 1b–1c, 1f, 18–25, 35a–35f, 36–41, 48a–48f
  independent, 8
  relating with equations, 48n, 49–53, 60a–60e
  representation on a coordinate grid, 7–9
Verbal description
  ACE, 7–16, 26–34, 42–47, 54–59
  of a relationship, 1b, 17f, 18–25, 35a–35f, 36–41, 48a–48f, 49–53, 60a–60e
Vocabulary, 1j

x-axis, 7–8
x-coordinate, 21

y-axis, 7–8
y-coordinate, 21

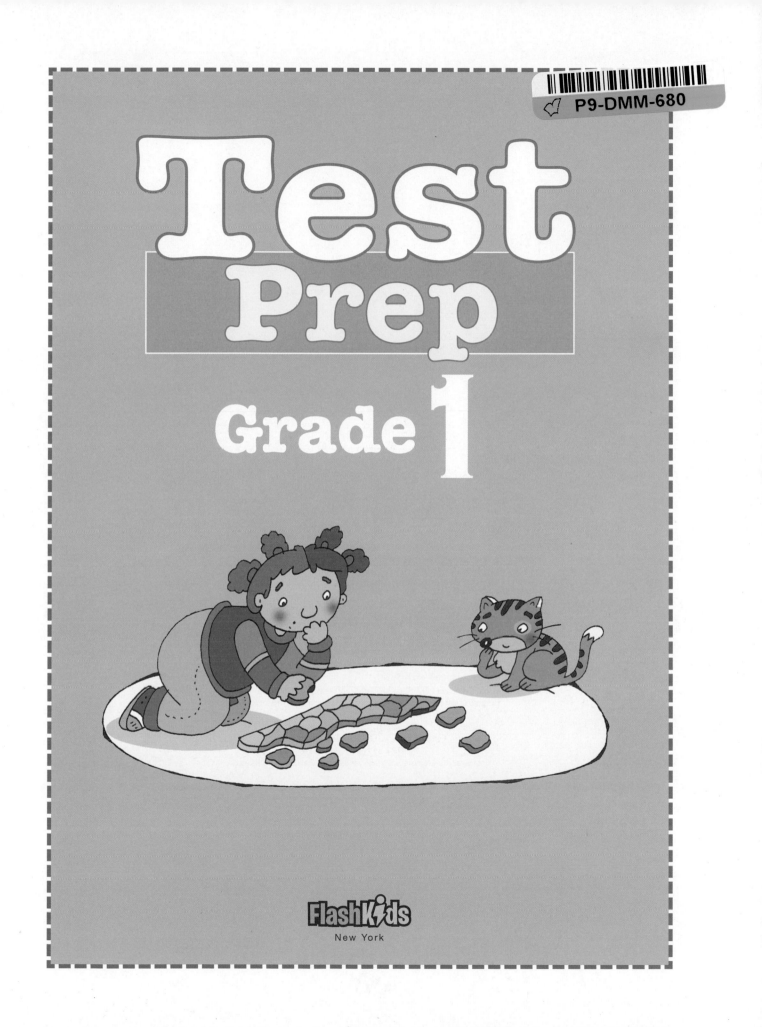

Test
Prep
Grade 1

FlashKids
New York

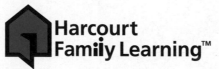

Harcourt
Family Learning™

© 2005 by Spark Publishing
Adapted from *Test Best for Test Prep, Level A*
© 1999 by Harcourt Achieve
Licensed under special arrangement with Harcourt Achieve.

For more information, please visit www.flashkids.com
Please submit all inquiries to Flashkids@sterlingpublishing.com

ISBN 978-1-4114-0397-0

Manufactured in China

Lot #:
14 16 18 20 19 17 15
04/18

Production by Creative Media Applications

TABLE OF CONTENTS

For Test-Smart Parents   4–7

Unit 1   Word Study Skills   8–13

Unit 2   Six Reading Skills   14–25

Unit 3   Reading Comprehension   26–33

Unit 4   Math Problem-Solving Plan   34–36

Unit 5   Math Problem Solving   37–51

Unit 6   Listening   52–63

Unit 7   Language   64–81

Unit 8   Practice Test 1: Word Study Skills   82–89

Unit 9   Practice Test 2: Reading Comprehension   90–97

Unit 10   Practice Test 3: Math Problem Solving   98–107

Unit 11   Practice Test 4: Math Procedures   108–113

Unit 12   Practice Test 5: Listening   114–119

Unit 13   Practice Test 6: Language   120–125

Answer Key   126–127

FOR TEST-SMART PARENTS

From the very first day of school, standardized tests become an important part of your child's school career. These tests are created by your state's education department and set to its standards of learning for each grade level. These tests are valuable tools that measure how much your child knows in the areas of math, reading, and writing. *Test Prep: Grade 1* is designed to help your child become familiar with what tests look like. This workbook will also help your child review the basic skills taught in the first grade.

Preparation is the key to helping your child become test-smart. Practicing basic skills in a testing situation can help ensure that your child's scores will reflect his or her understanding of the material presented in school. Test-smart students:

- are comfortable in the testing environment;
- know how to approach different kinds of test questions;
- apply knowledge to a variety of test formats;
- use time wisely during tests.

ABOUT THIS WORKBOOK

Test Prep: Grade 1 is divided into two helpful sections. Practice exercises and mini-tests introduce and review basic test-taking skills. At the end of the book are longer practice tests that mirror the actual tests your child will encounter at school.

- **Units 1–7: Mini-Tests**
  Each unit focuses on a subject found on standardized tests: word study skills, reading comprehension, mathematics, listening, and language. These mini-tests help your child learn specific test strategies. Most units conclude with a unit test that covers all of the skills in the unit's lessons.

- **Units 8–13: Practice Tests**
  These longer practice tests allow your child to apply test-taking skills in a realistic testing environment. You and your child will work together to simulate the actual experience of taking a standardized test. By familiarizing your child with the experience, these practice tests can lessen feelings of intimidation during school tests.

HOW TO USE THIS BOOK

Standardized testing in first grade always involves a teacher reading directions, examples, and stories to students. You will need to play the teacher's role.

Throughout this book, the text you will read aloud is printed in blue. This is true for both the practice and the test text. Every test begins with directions to share with your child. Many tests include additional information to read aloud, such as sentences or paragraphs.

From page 52 onward, most of the workbook features separate pages for adults. Read the directions on the left-hand page while your child completes the questions on the right-hand page. These activities will be enjoyable for both of you as you work together in the comfort of your home.

Look for Test Tips

Helpful Test Tips are located throughout this workbook. The Test Tips provide hints and ideas to help your child find the best answers. They do not appear in the final practice tests, which reflect realistic testing situations.

Find the Right Question

Make sure that your child is filling in the correct answer circles when answering test questions directly in the workbook. You might begin by asking your child to point to the question number and the answer choices. Also make sure that your child darkens the circles properly.

Do Not Rush

Help your child relax and take time to answer each question. Some first graders hurry to respond and may not read all of the answer choices carefully. Remind your child to slow down while taking the mini-tests in the first part of this book and read every answer before choosing one. Ask your child to explain why he or she chose each answer.

Four Principles of Test-Taking

These tests help your child develop four important skills that are crucial in testing situations. Familiarize yourself with these goals in order to support your child's development of these skills.

Using Time Wisely

All standardized tests are timed. Your child needs to understand how to manage time wisely. Review these strategies together:

- Work at a comfortable pace—try to imagine how much time is allowed to complete a section.
- Do not spend too much time on any one question.
- Mark items to return to if there is enough time.
- Use any remaining time to review answers.
- Use a watch to keep track of time.

Avoiding Errors

Your child can practice these strategies when choosing the correct answers on standardized tests:

- Pay careful attention to directions.
- Determine what is being asked.
- Mark answers in the appropriate place.
- Check all answers.
- Do not make stray marks on the answer sheet.

Reasoning

Standardized tests require your child to think logically when answering each question. These strategies can help your child think through each question before choosing the best answer:

- Before answering a question, read the entire question or passage and all the answer choices.
- Restate questions and answer choices in your own words.
- Apply skills learned in class and practice situations.

GUESSING

Your child can learn the best thing to do when the correct answer is not clear right away. Suggest these hints as helpful solutions if a question seems difficult:

- Try to answer all of the questions within the allotted time. Do not spend too much time on a question that seems hard.

- Eliminate answers that you know are incorrect. If you cannot do this, skip the question.

- Compare the remaining answers. Restate the question, and then choose the answer that seems most correct.

YEAR-ROUND SUPPORT FOR A TEST-SMART CHILD

With encouragement and support, your child will feel confident. Every student needs much experience with reading and exposure to a wide variety of reading matter. The school curriculum is carefully designed to teach skills your child needs to become a proficient learner. Your home environment is another essential part of the education equation. Here are some ways you can help your child year-round.

CREATE A QUIET STUDY SPACE

A quiet, clean, and cheerful study space will help your child develop strong study habits. Provide a study area with an open workspace. Make sure that writing supplies like paper and pencils are nearby, as well as tools like a calculator, ruler, scissors, glue, crayons, and a dictionary. You might also create files or boxes to store your child's work. Make separate files for finished works and works in progress.

BE A HOMEWORK HELPER

Talk about homework assignments with your child. Your questions can help your child focus on what is important about the task or project. Your interest in schoolwork will encourage your child's enthusiasm and dedication. Check in while your child is working to see if you can answer any questions or help find solutions. Just letting your child know that you care can promote active learning.

MAKE READING A FAMILY HABIT

Reading every day is an activity the family can enjoy together. It will also strengthen your child's performance in school. Careful attention to the reading process helps your child achieve success when taking both language arts and math tests. Together you can read passages from schoolwork or from books your child is currently enjoying. Add reading time to your family schedule, when family members read whatever they like. When the time is up, everyone can share an interesting new fact or quotation.

PRACTICE WITH A DICTIONARY

A children's dictionary designed especially for young readers is a helpful tool for learning about words and alphabetical order. When your child does not know the meaning of a word, encourage him or her to look it up in a dictionary. Help your child discover new words. You can try this game for fun. Take turns opening the dictionary to a random page. Read a definition aloud. Can your child guess the word?

TALK ABOUT TESTS

Find out from your child's teacher when standardized tests will be given during the school year. Mark the dates on your calendar so that both you and your child know when test day approaches. Try not to schedule big activities for the night before a test.

To prepare for the yearly standardized tests, score your child's work in this workbook together. Then talk about questions that were easy, hard, or tricky. Review any items your child answered incorrectly, and work together to understand why another answer is better.

BEFORE THE TEST

A GOOD NIGHT'S SLEEP

Your child will be more relaxed and alert after a full night of sleep. Some physical exercise before dinner can relieve feelings of stress. Do not place too much emphasis on the upcoming test, but answer any questions your child may have and provide reassurance that your child is ready for the test. Reminders of what to expect may lower anxiety. Help your child choose clothing for the next day, and have it ready so there is no last-minute hunting in the morning.

FOOD FOR THOUGHT

Studies show a direct link between eating a balanced breakfast and student performance. Children who eat a good breakfast are alert in class, concentrate well, and recall information. These skills are useful at any time of the year, but are especially helpful on test day. To make sure your child eats a balanced breakfast, wake up early enough to leave plenty of time for a relaxed meal together.

SUPPORT YOUR CHILD

Remind your child that standardized tests do not measure intelligence. They measure what your child knows about some subject. Make sure that your child understands that some words or ideas on the test may be unfamiliar. Tell your child not to become frustrated or angry if a question is hard but simply try to find the answer that makes the most sense. Do not set specific goals or offer rewards for high scores. Instead, assure your child that you will be happy with a positive and wholehearted effort. Doing one's best is what really counts!

AFTER THE TEST

Be sure to talk about the test score with your child. Remind your child that no single test score gives a complete picture of how much someone knows. Help your child set goals to maintain or improve test scores in the future. Always praise your child for working hard on a test. Test scores might suggest that your child needs improvement in a specific skill or subject. Talk with your child's teacher to find ways to support your child's growth in a particular area.

The text that appears in blue print is intended for an adult to read aloud.

Name the picture. Listen to the beginning sound. Read the words. Find the word with the same beginning sound.

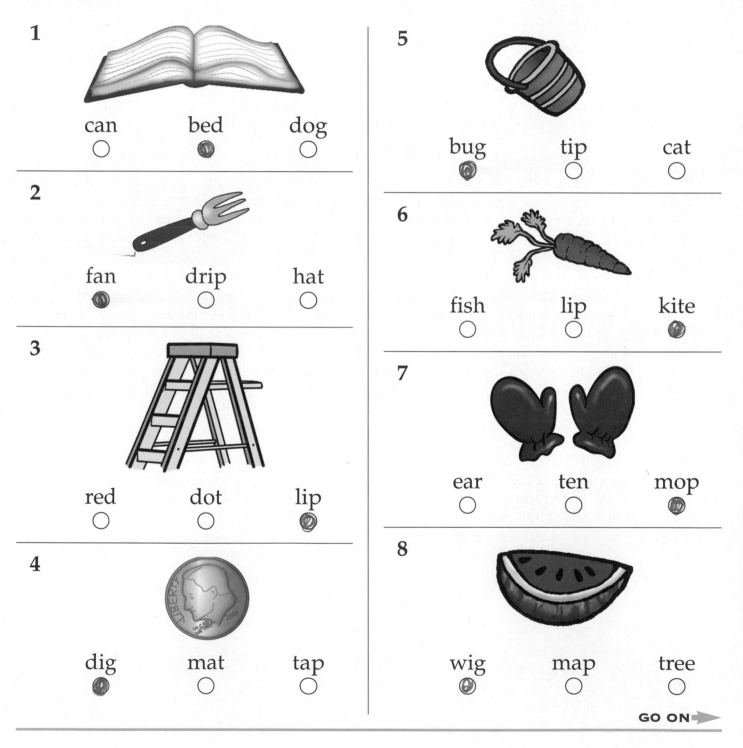

1

can ○   bed ●   dog ○

2

fan ●   drip ○   hat ○

3

red ○   dot ○   lip ●

4

dig ●   mat ○   tap ○

5

bug ●   tip ○   cat ○

6

fish ○   lip ○   kite ●

7

ear ○   ten ○   mop ●

8

wig ●   map ○   tree ○

GO ON

Read the word that names the picture. Listen to the ending sound. Read the words below it. Find the word with the same ending sound.

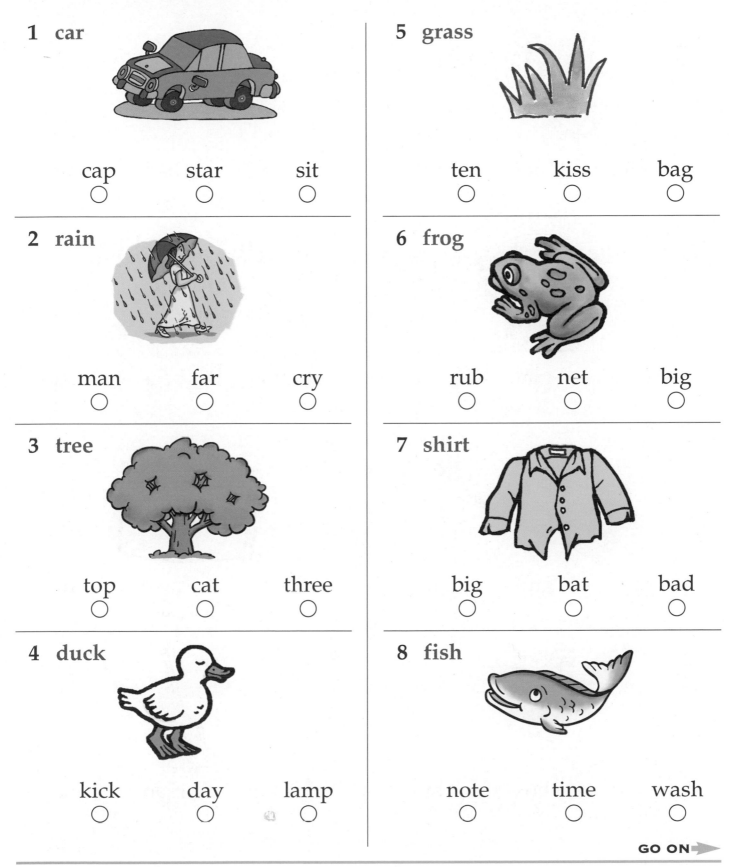

1 car

cap ○   star ○   sit ○

2 rain

man ○   far ○   cry ○

3 tree

top ○   cat ○   three ○

4 duck

kick ○   day ○   lamp ○

5 grass

ten ○   kiss ○   bag ○

6 frog

rub ○   net ○   big ○

7 shirt

big ○   bat ○   bad ○

8 fish

note ○   time ○   wash ○

GO ON ➡

Look at the picture. Find the word that names the picture.

1

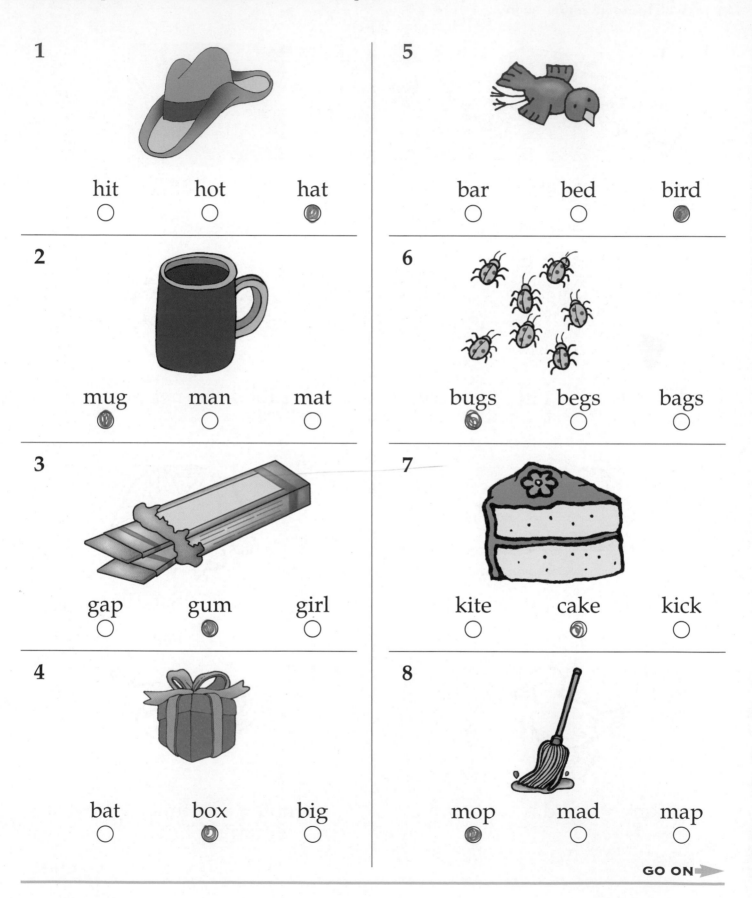

hit ○   hot ○   hat ◉

2

mug ◉   man ○   mat ○

3

gap ○   gum ◉   girl ○

4

bat ○   box ◉   big ○

5

bar ○   bed ○   bird ◉

6

bugs ◉   begs ○   bags ○

7

kite ○   cake ◉   kick ○

8

mop ◉   mad ○   map ○

GO ON ➡

Read the word. Find the word that rhymes.

1 bat

bite ○   cat ○   cab ○

2 can

pin ○   sit ○   tan ○

3 dress

clap ○   yes ○   fish ○

4 ten

men ○   tent ○   run ○

5 hot

coat ○   hop ○   pot ○

6 rip

lip ○   pig ○   pin ○

7 me

game ○   time ○   tree ○

8 top

two ○   hop ○   toy ○

9 look

owl ○   log ○   cook ○

10 note

boat ○   fan ○   nine ○

STOP

Name the picture. Listen to the beginning sound. Read the words. Find the word with the same beginning sound.

1

pup ○   box ○   dip ○

2

ant ○   nail ○   snow ○

3

book ○   tape ○   pop ○

4

tip ○   sit ○   nap ○

Read the word that names the picture. Listen to the ending sound. Read the words below it. Find the word with the same ending sound.

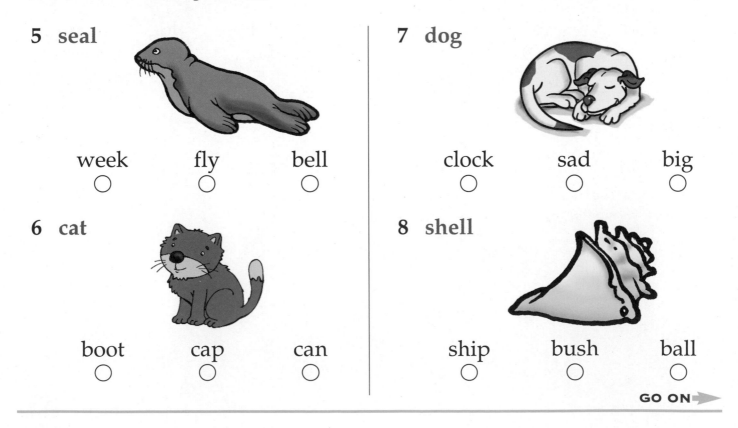

5 seal

week ○   fly ○   bell ○

6 cat

boot ○   cap ○   can ○

7 dog

clock ○   sad ○   big ○

8 shell

ship ○   bush ○   ball ○

GO ON ➡

Look at the picture. Find the word that names the picture.

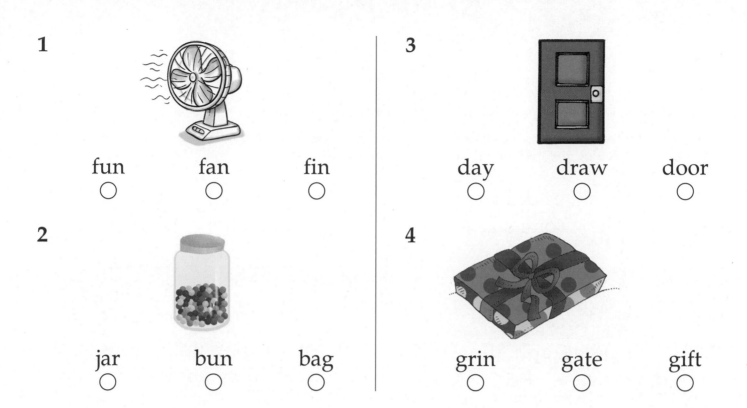

1

fun   fan   fin
○   ○   ○

2

jar   bun   bag
○   ○   ○

3

day   draw   door
○   ○   ○

4

grin   gate   gift
○   ○   ○

Read the word. Find the word that rhymes.

5 plays

   miss   days   cross
   ○   ○   ○

6 fly

   trip   tree   try
   ○   ○   ○

7 swim

   ham   him   hum
   ○   ○   ○

8 plate

   eat   seat   great
   ○   ○   ○

STOP

SIX READING SKILLS

SKILL 1: DETERMINING WORD MEANINGS

The text that appears in blue print is intended for an adult to read aloud.

Sometimes you can use word clues to find the meaning of a new word. Read along as I read these paragraphs. Try to find the meaning of the underlined word.

The new shoes did not fit. They were the <u>wrong</u> size.

1 In this paragraph, the word **wrong** means —

   ○ too big.

   ◉ not right.

   ○ the same.

David won <u>first</u> prize in the spelling bee. He spelled every word right.

2 In this paragraph, the word <u>first</u> means —

   ◉ the best.

   ○ in front.

   ○ before.

Sula cannot find her brother. She <u>peeked</u> into his room to see if he was there.

3 In this paragraph, the word **peeked** means —

   ○ called.

   ◉ looked.

   ○ walked.

The teacher wanted her book back. She asked if I had <u>finished</u> reading it yet.

4 In this paragraph, the word <u>finished</u> means —

   ○ still.

   ○ liked.

   ◉ done.

GO ON ➡

The school bus came to a stop. There was a red light.

5 **In this paragraph, the word stop means —**

○ get on.

○ get off.

◉ wait.

Ming turned the wheel. We watched it spin.

6 **In this paragraph, the word spin means —**

◉ go around.

○ roll away.

○ go for a ride.

TEST TIP

Ask your child to explain the "clue" that led to each correct answer.

The teacher did not want us to run. She told us to walk slowly.

7 **In this paragraph, the word slowly means —**

○ at once.

◉ not fast.

○ not slow.

Marta's job was to greet people. She stood at the door as they came into the room. She was smiling as she welcomed them.

8 **In this paragraph, the word greet means —**

◉ to say hello.

○ to say good-bye.

○ to check.

STOP

The main idea is the meaning of the story. The main idea is often stated in the story. Read along as I read these stories. Then try to find the main idea.

Did you know that some birds can talk? Some parrots can talk. They say what they hear. Sometimes, they say things at the wrong time.

I have a parrot. It was a birthday present. My parrot says many things. One day, my mother was telling me to pick up my toys. The parrot said, "Be quiet!" Mom gave me a funny look. She told me to clean my room. "Be quiet!" said the parrot.

Mom got so angry that she told me to stay in my room for the rest of the day.

1 What is the main idea of this story?

- ○ Parrots make great gifts.
- ○ It is important to keep your room clean.
- ● Parrots can say things at the wrong time.

Hint: Think about the whole story. Look at the first paragraph.

TEST TIP

To help your child find the main idea, ask, "What is the big idea in this story?" Read each answer choice aloud. Talk about whether each answer choice states the main idea.

TEST TIP

The Hints will help your child find the correct answer. Read them aloud if your child is having difficulty finding the answer.

GO ON

Ricka says she wants to be an animal doctor. She loves all kinds of animals. She has three pets. She has two dogs and one cat.

Ricka takes care of all her pets. She makes sure that they eat well. She sees that they get plenty of rest and play. She brushes their fur. She does everything the animal doctor tells her to do.

I think that Ricka will be a good animal doctor one day.

2 **What is the main idea of this story?**

○ Ricka takes care of her three pets.

○ Ricka wants to be an animal doctor.

○ Ricka listens to the animal doctor.

Hint: What does the whole story talk about?

Facts and ideas are important. By finding them, you will know what the story is about. Read this story with me. Then answer the questions.

Tina and her family went to the beach last summer. One day, they went to see a lighthouse.

Mr. Beal, the man who worked at the lighthouse, told Tina all about it. The lighthouse is 90 years old. It is all white and it is 120 feet tall. It has a strong light. Sailors can see the light as far as 24 miles out at sea.

1 Tina and her family went to —

○ the city.

○ the beach.

○ the country.

Hint: Look at the first sentence.

2 Who is Mr. Beal?

○ a sailor

○ Tina's father

○ the man who works at the lighthouse

Hint: Read the second paragraph.

3 How tall is the lighthouse?

○ 90 feet

○ 120 feet

○ 24 feet

Hint: Look for the sentence that talks about how tall the lighthouse is.

TEST TIP

Help your child answer the questions by rereading sections from the story.

GO ON

It is helpful to put events in the order in which they happen. Read each story with me. Then answer the questions about what happened first, next, and last.

"What's the matter, Lucy?" asked her teacher.

"I lost my new gloves. I looked everywhere, but I can't find them."

When it was time to go home, Lucy put on her coat. She put her hands in her pockets. Then she started to smile. There in her pockets were her gloves, just where she had left them.

1 **Which of these happened first in the story?**

○ Lucy found her gloves.

○ Lucy lost her gloves.

○ Lucy looked for her gloves.

Hint: Look at the beginning of the story.

2 **When did Lucy put on her coat?**

○ when it was time to go home

○ when Lucy lost her gloves

○ when Lucy looked for her gloves

Hint: Look at the last paragraph.

3 **Which of these happened last in the story?**

○ Lucy put her hands in her pockets.

○ Lucy told the teacher she couldn't find her gloves.

○ Lucy found her gloves.

Hint: Look at the last paragraph.

TEST TIP

Emphasize signal words if you need to reread the story. Help your child recognize the meanings of words like *one day* and *then*.

GO ON ➡

Yuko and Rosa were playing outside. They saw a dog across the street. Just then Mr. Jackson came outside.

"Look at that poor little dog, Mr. Jackson. He looks hungry. What can we do to help him?" asked Yuko.

"I'll get him some food," said Mr. Jackson. He went inside and came back out with some food for the dog.

4 Which of these happened first in the story?

- ○ Mr. Jackson gave the dog some food.
- ○ Yuko and Rosa were playing outside.
- ○ The girls saw a dog.

Hint: Look at the beginning of the story.

5 When did Mr. Jackson get the dog some food?

- ○ when he saw the girls playing outside
- ○ when his sister asked him to
- ○ when the girls asked him for help

Hint: Look at the second paragraph.

6 Which of these happened last in the story?

- ○ The dog was given food.
- ○ Yuko and Rosa saw a dog.
- ○ Mr. Jackson came outside.

Hint: Look at the end of the story.

TEST TIP

After your child selects an answer, reread it and ask your child to explain why that answer is correct. Talking about answers can help your child find and correct mistakes.

Knowing what happened and why it happened helps you understand stories. Read these stories with me. Think about why things happen.

After Kenji was born, Grandma came to visit from Japan. She met my new brother Kenji for the first time. I think she likes him better than she likes me.

Everyone in my family likes Kenji because he is so cute. They talk about him all day. I like him, too, but I want my family to like me again. I came first. I am five years old. I have a lot to talk about. Kenji cannot talk. He just sleeps all day.

1 Why did Grandma come to visit?

○ She wanted to move from Japan.

○ She wanted to see the new baby.

○ She wanted to take a trip.

Hint: What happened that made Grandma come to visit?

2 Why does everyone like Kenji?

○ He's a cute little baby.

○ He is the first child.

○ He sleeps a lot.

Hint: What is it about Kenji that everyone likes?

TEST TIP

You might explain the words *cause* and *effect*. The reason why something happened is the *cause*. The thing that happens is the *effect*.

GO ON ➡

Julia could not run very fast. She could not run as fast as the others. She wanted to do better. Every day she tried running faster and faster. Soon she was able to run so fast that she won a race. She was very happy.

TEST TIP

Make sure your child looks for an answer that tells *why* something happened. In question 3, your child might choose the first answer because Julia is happy at the end of the story. Point out that Julia does not run because she is happy. She runs for a different reason. Read the other answer choices to find the reason why Julia runs.

3 Why does Julia run every day?

○ She is happy.

○ She likes to run.

○ She wants to run faster.

Hint: What makes Julia run every day?

4 Why is Julia happy?

○ She won a race.

○ It is her birthday.

○ She cannot run as fast as the others.

Hint: What made Julia happy at the end of the story?

Sometimes you can tell what might happen next. Read these stories with me. Think about what would make sense if the story kept going.

Tricia cannot decide how to spend her money. She got ten dollars for her birthday. She has had the money a month. She has not spent it yet. There are many things she wants to buy.

She wants to buy a book. She likes books with many pretty pictures. She likes books about animals.

She wants to buy a puzzle, too. She likes the ones with many pieces. She spreads the pieces all over the floor. It takes a long time to finish it.

1 What will happen next?

- ○ Tricia will buy some stuffed animals.

- ○ Tricia will ask for some more money.

- ○ Tricia will buy a book or a puzzle.

Hint: Think about what Tricia wants to buy with her money.

TEST TIP

Help your child choose the answer that makes sense. Explain that the details in the story are leading somewhere. Ask these questions:

- What did Tricia get for her birthday?
- What does she like?

GO ON

Mia's aunt likes to collect things. She collects tiny glass animals. She has two dogs and three cats all made of glass. She has them on a shelf above her table. They are pretty to look at.

Mia's aunt also collects dolls. She has many dolls. Some of them wear fancy costumes. They come from many different countries.

Mia's aunt is coming to visit next week. Mia would like to buy her something.

2 What will Mia do tomorrow?

○ visit her aunt

○ go shopping for a gift

○ stay home from school

Hint: Read the last paragraph.

TEST TIP

Ask these questions to help your child make the best prediction:

• Does Mia like her aunt? How do you know?

• What is going to happen next week?

• What will Mia probably do next?

STOP

What a character says and thinks tells you what that person feels. Read these stories with me. Think about how the characters feel.

Patrick thinks his cat should have a collar. His cat likes to go outside. Sometimes the cat is gone for a long time. What if the cat cannot find his way home? Patrick decides to buy his cat a collar. Patrick's name and phone number will be on the collar. The cat's name will be on the collar, too.

1 Why does Patrick want his cat to have a new collar?

○ The cat will be happier with one.

○ He is afraid his cat will get lost.

○ The collar he has now is very old.

Hint: Why is Patrick worried?

Maine is a great place to visit. You can go swimming in the ocean. There are sandy beaches. There are many mountains too. You can go walking in the woods. You can climb up the mountains. When you get to the top you can see things far away. There are many fun things to do in Maine.

2 What do you know about the boy telling this story?

○ He likes to play baseball.

○ He is a good swimmer.

○ He likes to go to Maine.

Hint: Read the whole story. Look at the first and last sentences.

READING COMPREHENSION

SOLVING RIDDLES

The text that appears in blue print is intended for an adult to read aloud.

Read these riddles with me. Find the picture that shows what the sentences tell.

1

I can be seen in the sky.
I can be seen at night.

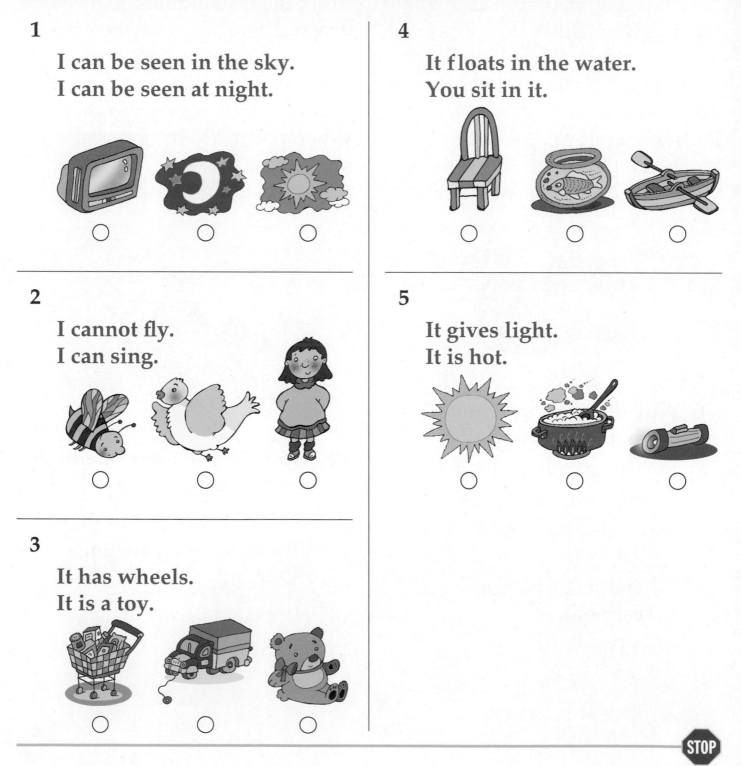

4

It floats in the water.
You sit in it.

2

I cannot fly.
I can sing.

5

It gives light.
It is hot.

3

It has wheels.
It is a toy.

STOP

26

Look at the picture. Then read these sentences with me. Find the word that best completes the sentence.

1 Cara and her mother are sitting on a

    lap   bed   chair
    ○   ○   ○

2 Cara's mother is reading her a

    letter   newspaper book
    ○   ○   ○

3 Cara listens to her mother's

    song   voice   shout
    ○   ○   ○

4 Julio is making

    salad   soup   pancakes
    ○   ○   ○

5 He is wearing a cook's

    hat   sign   coat
    ○   ○   ○

6 Andy could not find his

    shoe   brother   pet
    ○   ○   ○

7 Andy looked under his

    bed   desk   pillow
    ○   ○   ○

8 There he found his

    rabbit   turtle   duck
    ○   ○   ○

STOP

27

Read these stories with me. Then answer the questions about the story.

Manny Helps Out

Manny likes to help his family. He is only four years old. He thinks he can do things his big brother can do. He wants to help his dad. His dad is painting the house. His dad gives Manny paint and a brush.

Manny gets paint all over his clothes. Dad says, "You will do better when you are five." Manny says, "I don't want to paint anymore. I want to have some fun." Dad laughs.

1 **Manny's brother is**
   ○ older than Manny.
   ○ younger than Manny.
   ○ the same age as Manny.

2 **Why does Manny want to paint the house?**
   ○ He is a good painter.
   ○ He wants to help his dad.
   ○ He does not like the color of the house.

3 **What happens to Manny's clothes?**
   ○ He tears them.
   ○ He washes them.
   ○ He gets paint on them.

4 **What might happen next in the story?**
   ○ Manny will paint more.
   ○ Manny will go out to play.
   ○ Manny will wash all of his clothes.

GO ON

Peppy

We have a new dog at our house. His name is Peppy. He is two years old. My sister and I like to play with Peppy. We throw a ball, and he brings it back. We take him for walks on our street. Peppy barks when he is hungry. I put food in his bowl. My sister gives him cool water. We take good care of Peppy.

5 How old is Peppy?

_____

_____

_____

6 You can tell that the children
- ○ are unhappy with Peppy.
- ○ love Peppy.
- ○ are afraid of Peppy.

7 When does Peppy bark?
- ○ when he wants food
- ○ when he goes for a walk
- ○ when he is tired

8 This story tells about
- ○ two children and their new pet.
- ○ a man and his cat.
- ○ how to find a dog.

STOP

Read these riddles with me. Find the pictures that show what the sentences tell about.

1 I can smile.
I cannot walk.

○   ○   ○

2 It can fly.
It takes people places.

○   ○   ○

3 I can play games.
I wear clothes.

○   ○   ○

4 It is green.
It is an animal.

○   ○   ○

5 It is silver.
You can eat with it.

○   ○   ○

6 It is hot.
You plug it in.

○   ○   ○

7 It is clothing.
It is worn on the feet.

○   ○   ○

GO ON ➡

Look at each picture. Then read these sentences with me. Find the word that best completes the sentences.

8 Two actors are on a

stage ○   train ○   horse ○

9 The people watching will

sing ○   talk ○   clap ○

10 They will leave when the play is

over ○   beginning ○   written ○

11 Ted and Luis are putting up a

table ○   house ○   tent ○

12 Soon they will be

finished ○   arriving ○   rested ○

13 Sadako is wearing her mother's

coat ○   dress ○   gloves ○

14 She is having a lot of

trouble ○   visitors ○   fun ○

15 Sadako is

talking ○   crying ○   smiling ○

GO ON ➡

Rita's Find

One day Rita found a baby bird in the yard. There was no nest nearby. There was no mother bird.

Rita picked up the tiny bird. She kept it for three weeks. The bird grew strong.

Rita took the bird outside. It flew to a nearby tree. It began to sing. Rita knew that her bird would be fine.

16 Where did Rita find the bird?

_____

- - - - - - - - - - - - - - - - - - -

_____

17 Why did Rita take care of the bird?

○ Its mother was gone.

○ She liked to sing.

○ Rita's teacher told her to keep it.

18 Why did the bird fly to a nearby tree?

○ It wanted to hide.

○ It saw its mother.

○ It was ready to take care of itself.

19 You can tell that Rita is

○ kind.

○ silly.

○ unhappy.

GO ON

Elephants

Have you ever seen an elephant? The elephant has a very long nose. It is called a trunk. The elephant's trunk weighs about 300 pounds. Elephants can use their trunks to smell. Elephants use their trunks to hold things, too. They can hold up to 600 pounds. Elephants also use their trunks to reach food. Their trunks help them grab leaves high up in trees. They pull grasses from the ground. Elephants use their trunks in many ways.

20 **What is an elephant's nose called?**

○ a beak

○ a bill

○ a trunk

21 **How many pounds can elephants hold with their trunks?**

_____

_____

22 **This story tells some ways that elephants**

○ take baths.

○ use their trunks.

○ take care of their babies.

23 **For an elephant, the trunk is very**

○ important.

○ dusty.

○ light.

TEST TIP

Reread sentences from the story to help your child answer the questions.

MATH PROBLEM-SOLVING PLAN

OVERVIEW

THE PROBLEM-SOLVING PLAN

The text that appears in blue print is intended for an adult to read aloud.

Math problems are sometimes in words, like a story. Having a plan can help you decide how to find the answer. Here are the steps to do these math problems:

STEP 1: WHAT IS THE QUESTION?
Read the problem. Can you see what you must find?
What is being asked?

STEP 2: FIND THE FACTS
Find the facts:
  A. IMPORTANT FACTS are facts you need to do the problem.
  B. FACTS YOU DON'T NEED are facts not needed to do the problem.
  C. ARE MORE FACTS NEEDED? Do you need more facts to do the problem?

STEP 3: GET A PLAN
Choose a way to do the problem.

STEP 4: DO THE PROBLEM
Use your plan to do the problem.

STEP 5: DOES YOUR ANSWER MAKE SENSE?
Read the problem again.
Does your answer make sense?

GO ON ➡

Read the word problem with me. Then we'll work through each step together to find the answer to this math story.

Tania wants to buy a new fish tank. The one in the store can hold up to 15 fish. She has 6 goldfish and 5 guppies. Will this tank be large enough for all her fish?

STEP 1: WHAT IS THE QUESTION?

_____

_ _ _ _ _ _ _ _ _ _ _ _ _ _ _ _ _ _ _ _

_____

STEP 2: FIND THE FACTS

_____

_ _ _ _ _ _ _ _ _ _ _ _ _ _ _ _ _ _ _ _

_____

STEP 3: GET A PLAN

_____

_ _ _ _ _ _ _ _ _ _ _ _ _ _ _ _ _ _ _ _

_____

STEP 4: DO THE PROBLEM

_____

_ _ _ _ _ _ _ _ _ _ _ _ _ _ _ _ _ _ _ _

_____

STEP 5: DOES YOUR ANSWER MAKE SENSE?

_____

_ _ _ _ _ _ _ _ _ _ _ _ _ _ _ _ _ _ _ _

_____

GO ON ➡

Read the word problem with me. Then we'll work through each step together to find the answer to this math story.

Kyle feeds the lions in the zoo. It takes him 5 minutes to prepare the food for each lion. He starts feeding the lions at 12:00 noon. At what time will he begin to feed the 3rd lion?

STEP 1: WHAT IS THE QUESTION?

STEP 2: FIND THE FACTS

STEP 3: GET A PLAN

STEP 4: DO THE PROBLEM

STEP 5: DOES YOUR ANSWER MAKE SENSE?

STOP

MATH PROBLEM SOLVING

UNDERSTANDING NUMERATION

The text that appears in blue print is intended for an adult to read aloud.

46842
hu tens ones

1 Fill in the circle under the number ninety-four.

49   90   94   904
○   ○   ◉   ○

---

2 Which number has 2 in the tens place?

427   472   4,072   247
◉   ○   ○   ○

---

3 Which bird is third from the clouds?

○   ◉   ○   ○

---

4 Look at the blocks. How many blocks are there altogether?

302   23   13   32
○   ○   ○   ◉

---

5 Write the number that is 10 less than the number on the door.

21

eleven

STOP

1 Which pot has three out of its five flowers shaded?

○   ○   ○   ○

2 Which shape is divided into four equal parts?

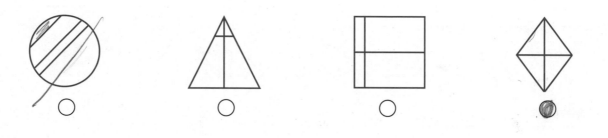

○   ○   ○   ⊙

3 Which number sentence is equal to the number sentence in the box?

$$4 + 3 = 7$$

(handwritten: 7, triangle with 4 and 3, 4+3=7, 7-3=4, 3+4=7, 7-4=3)

$3 + 7 = 10$ $7 - 2 = 5$ $4 - 3 = 1$ $7 - 3 = 4$
○   ○   ○   ⊙

4 Which number goes in the box to make the number sentence correct?

$5 + 0 = \square$ 10   5   0   1
                        ○   ⊙   ○   ○

STOP

1 Look for a pattern. Which number belongs in the empty box?

| 3 | 6 | 9 | | 15 |

10 ○   12 ○   14 ○   20 ○

---

2 Mrs. Inez numbered all the playground balls. This picture shows some of the balls in order. Fill in the circle under the ball that Mrs. Inez will mark number 29.

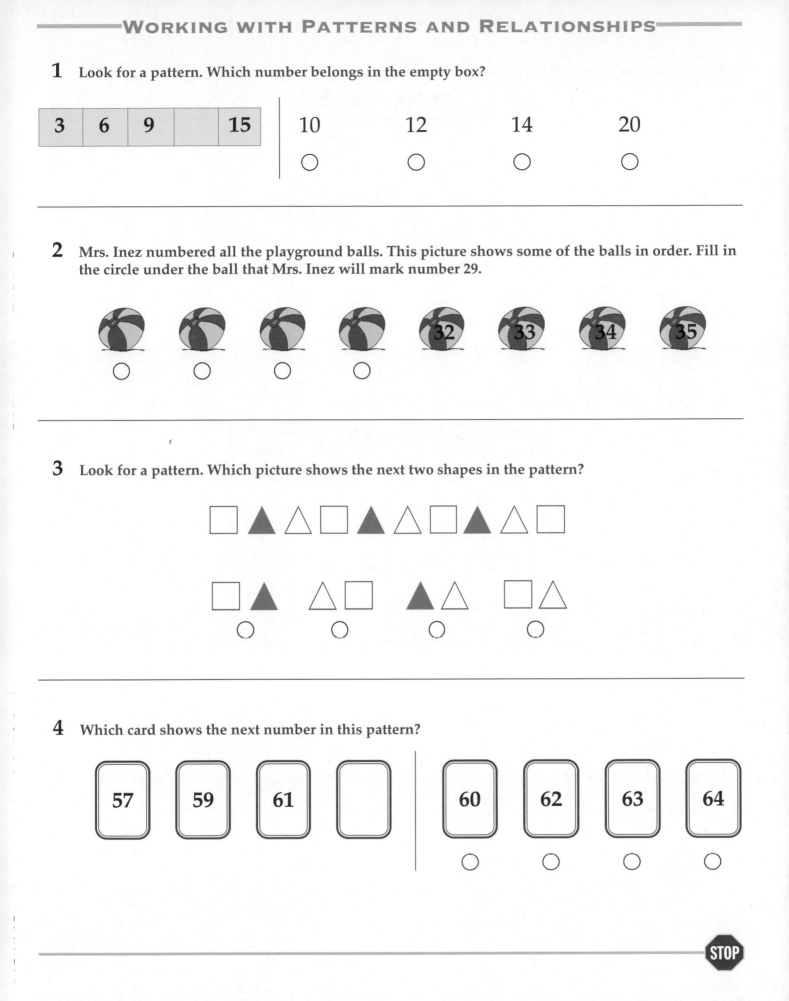

32   33   34   35

○   ○   ○   ○

---

3 Look for a pattern. Which picture shows the next two shapes in the pattern?

□ ▲ △ □ ▲ △ □ ▲ △ □

□ ▲   △ □   ▲ △   □ △
○   ○   ○   ○

---

4 Which card shows the next number in this pattern?

| 57 | 59 | 61 | |

| 60 | 62 | 63 | 64 |
  ○   ○   ○   ○

STOP

1 Look at this graph. Which player won only five games?

Games Won	
Karen	IIII
Ling	NN
Delia	NN I
Steven	NN III

Karen ○   Ling ○   Delia ○   Steven ○

---

2 Look at this chart. How many animal stories did Toby read?

Reading Chart		
Kind of Book	Jerry	Toby
Adventure	3	2
Animal	2	5
Poetry	1	1

_____

_____

---

3 Ron plays a game with paper shapes. He puts one square, four triangles, six circles, and two diamonds into a box. Without looking, Ron picks one shape. Which shape is he most likely to pick?

○   ○   ○   ○

STOP

1 Look at the first shape. Which shape to the right is exactly the same shape?

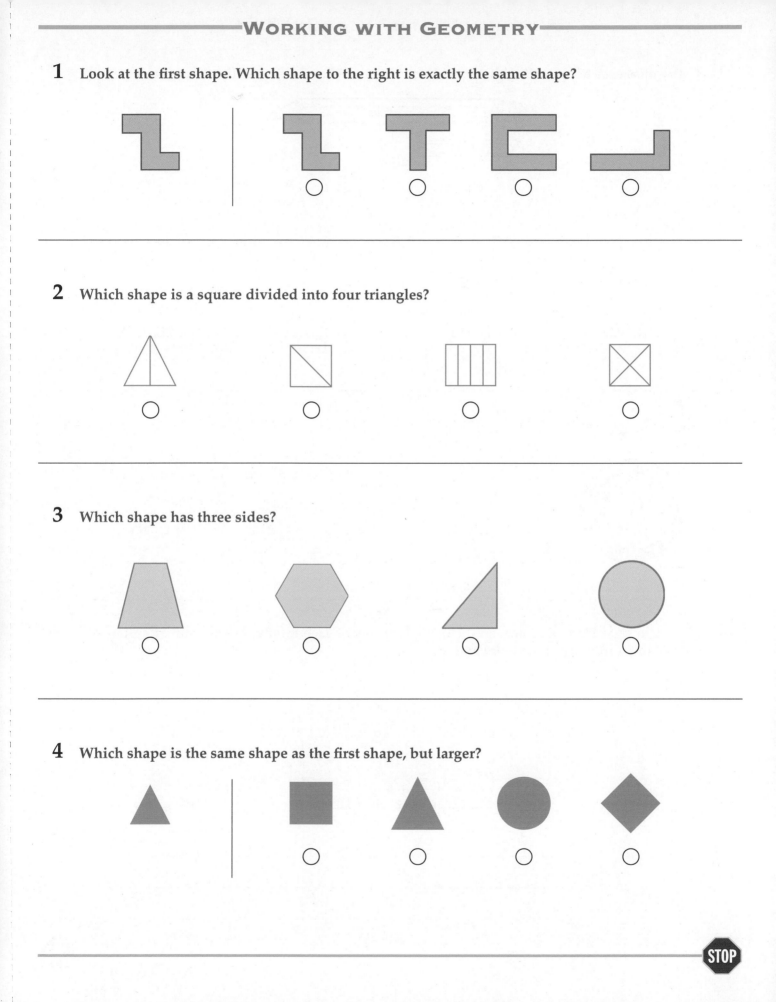

○   ○   ○   ○

2 Which shape is a square divided into four triangles?

○   ○   ○   ○

3 Which shape has three sides?

○   ○   ○   ○

4 Which shape is the same shape as the first shape, but larger?

○   ○   ○   ○

1 Cathy measures her pencil with paper clips. About how many paper clips long is this pencil?

2   4   5   9
○   ○   ○   ○

---

2 Which unit would you use to measure the weight of a crayon?

inches   tons   pounds   ounces
○   ○   ○   ○

---

3 What time does the clock show?

6:30   7:30   8:30   9:30
○   ○   ○   ○

---

4 Mr. Gallo's garden club meets on the third Saturday of each month. Look at the calendar. Write the date of the third Saturday of November.

November

Sun	Mon	Tues	Wed	Thur	Fri	Sat
			1	2	3	4
5	6	7	8	9	10	11
12	13	14	15	16	17	18
19	20	21	22	23	24	25
26	27	28	29	30		

_____

STOP

1 I am thinking of a number that is more than 12 and less than 25. It has a 3 in it. Which of these numbers am I thinking of?

30 ○   23 ○   17 ○   3 ○

2 I am thinking of a number that is less that 38. You say its name when you count by fives. It has a 2 in it. Which of these numbers am I thinking of?

20 ○   27 ○   35 ○   40 ○

3 Ted sees nine ducks in the pond. Then four of the ducks swim to the other side of the pond. How many ducks are left? Fill in the circle under the number sentence that shows how to find the number of ducks that are left.

○ 9 − 4 = ☐   ○ 5 + 4 = ☐

○ ☐ − 4 = 5   ○ 5 − 4 = ☐

 STOP

The answer choice NH means that the answer is not here.

1 Rita saw 10 ducks swimming in the pond. She also saw 5 ducks standing near the pond. How many ducks did Rita see altogether?

4 ○   15 ○   18 ○   NH ○

2 Ira put 7 oranges in a bag. He put 12 oranges in another bag. How many oranges did Ira have altogether?

7   12

19 ○   9 ○   5 ○   NH ○

3 Mrs. Ling has 15 calculators on a shelf in her store. Then she sells 2 calculators. How many calculators does Mrs. Ling have left?

15   2

2 ○   8 ○   38 ○   NH ○

4 Tamiko has five plain shirts. She has three striped shirts. Write the number that tells how many shirts Tamiko has altogether.

5   3

_ _

Find the answer to each addition or subtraction problem. Choose NH if the answer is not here.

1 $7 + 7 = \square$

0	12	14	NH
○	○	○	○

2 $6 + 4 = \square$

10	5	2	NH
○	○	○	○

3
$$\begin{array}{r} 3 \\ 8 \\ + 4 \\ \hline \end{array}$$

13	14	15	NH
○	○	○	○

4
$$\begin{array}{r} 65 \\ + 3 \\ \hline \end{array}$$

5
$$\begin{array}{r} 30 \\ + 27 \\ \hline \end{array}$$

17	37	57	NH
○	○	○	○

6 $8 - 5 = \square$

10	4	3	NH
○	○	○	○

7
$$\begin{array}{r} 14 \\ - 5 \\ \hline \end{array}$$

9	10	19	NH
○	○	○	○

8
$$\begin{array}{r} 43 \\ - 3 \\ \hline \end{array}$$

9
$$\begin{array}{r} 78 \\ - 21 \\ \hline \end{array}$$

99	69	57	NH
○	○	○	○

10
$$\begin{array}{r} 460 \\ - 30 \\ \hline \end{array}$$

430	400	490	NH
○	○	○	○

TEST TIP

Remind your child to look at the plus or minus sign to decide whether to add or subtract.

1 Write the number that goes in the box to make the number sentence correct.

$\Box + 7 = 9$

— —

---

2 Which numbers both have a three in the ones place?

34, 13   34, 31   43, 13   43, 31
○   ○   ○   ○

---

3 Which number is more than 49 and less than 72?

49 $\Box$ 72   81   73   57   48
                      ○   ○   ○   ○

---

4 Which number means the same as 20 + 5?

20 + 5   205   75   25   7
                 ○   ○   ○   ○

---

5 Leo uses leaves to measure a rake. About how many leaves long is the rake?

4   6   9   16
○   ○   ○   ○

GO ON ➡

6 Which circle has one of its six parts shaded?

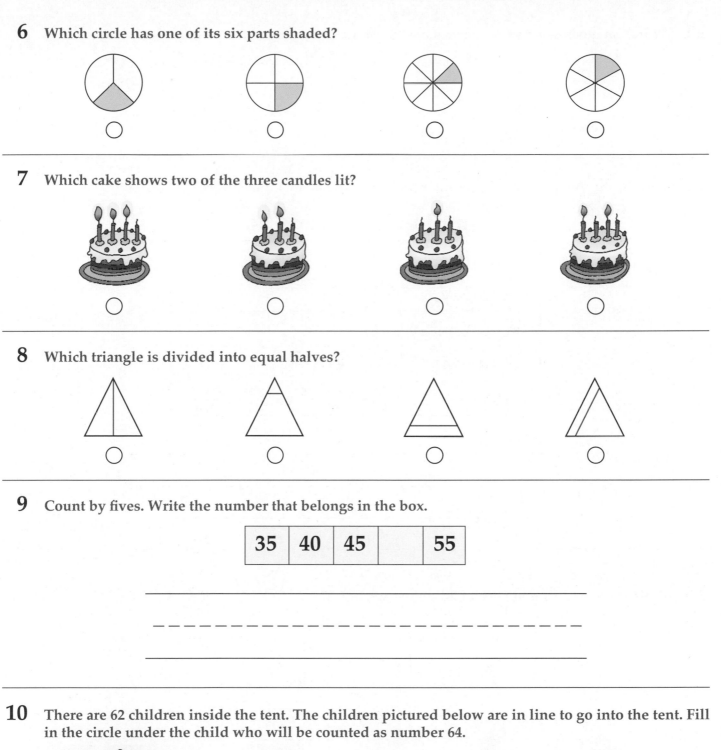

7 Which cake shows two of the three candles lit?

8 Which triangle is divided into equal halves?

9 Count by fives. Write the number that belongs in the box.

35	40	45		55

_____

- -

_____

10 There are 62 children inside the tent. The children pictured below are in line to go into the tent. Fill in the circle under the child who will be counted as number 64.

62

GO ON ➡

11 Which shape is exactly the same as the one at the beginning of the row?

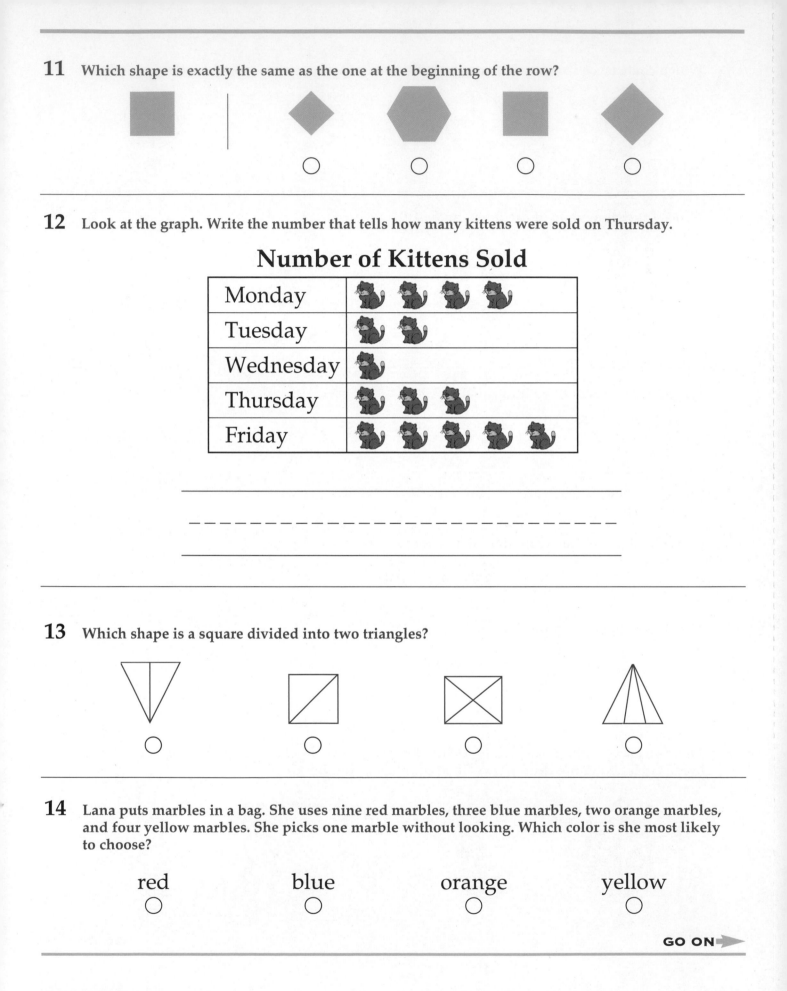

12 Look at the graph. Write the number that tells how many kittens were sold on Thursday.

Number of Kittens Sold

Monday	🐱 🐱 🐱 🐱
Tuesday	🐱 🐱
Wednesday	🐱
Thursday	🐱 🐱 🐱
Friday	🐱 🐱 🐱 🐱 🐱

_____

- -

_____

13 Which shape is a square divided into two triangles?

14 Lana puts marbles in a bag. She uses nine red marbles, three blue marbles, two orange marbles, and four yellow marbles. She picks one marble without looking. Which color is she most likely to choose?

red   blue   orange   yellow

GO ON

15 I am thinking of a number. It is more than 8 and less than 20. It has a 9 in it. Which of these numbers am I thinking of?

       4   15   19   29

       ○   ○   ○   ○

16 Four frogs are sitting on a log. Two more frogs jump on the log. Fill in the circle under the number sentence that shows how to find the number of frogs that are now on the log.

○   4 + 2 = ☐   ○   4 − 2 = ☐

○   6 + 2 = ☐   ○   6 − ☐ = 2

17 Which shape has exactly four corners?

      ○   ○   ○   ○

18 Anton baked six square cookies and five round cookies. How many cookies did Anton bake?

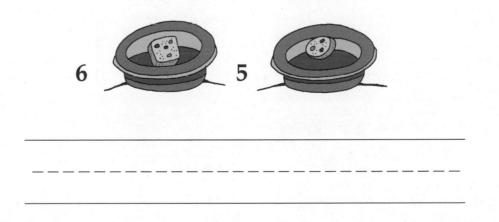

6   5

_____

- -

_____

GO ON ➡

19 Misha counted 15 butterflies in the garden. Then he counted 4 more. How many butterflies did Misha count in all?

15   **4**

29   19   11   NH
○   ○   ○   ○

20 There are 15 trumpet players in the school band. There are 8 drummers. How many more trumpet players are there than drummers?

15   **8**

7   9   23   NH
○   ○   ○   ○

21 Claire is at the beach. She collects 26 shells. She puts 3 shells back because they are broken. How many shells does Claire have left?

26   **3**

22   29   32   NH
○   ○   ○   ○

22 Mia took 24 balloons to school. She gave away 20 of the balloons. How many balloons did Mia have left?

24   **20**

20   14   4   NH
○   ○   ○   ○

GO ON

Find the answer to each addition or subtraction problem.

23
$$\begin{array}{r} 2 \\ 9 \\ +\ 3 \\ \hline \end{array}$$

24 ○ 14 ○ 12 ○ NH ○

24
$$\begin{array}{r} 66 \\ +\ 3 \\ \hline \end{array}$$

_____

- - - - - - - - - - - - - - - - - - -

_____

25
$$\begin{array}{r} 38 \\ +\ 40 \\ \hline \end{array}$$

48 ○ 58 ○ 68 ○ NH ○

26
$$\begin{array}{r} 72 \\ +\ 20 \\ \hline \end{array}$$

92 ○ 52 ○ 50 ○ NH ○

27 $5 - 5 = \square$

5 ○ 1 ○ 0 ○ NH ○

28
$$\begin{array}{r} 11 \\ -\ 3 \\ \hline \end{array}$$

6 ○ 7 ○ 8 ○ NH ○

29
$$\begin{array}{r} 58 \\ -\ 6 \\ \hline \end{array}$$

2 ○ 22 ○ 52 ○ NH ○

30
$$\begin{array}{r} 80 \\ -\ 20 \\ \hline \end{array}$$

_____

- - - - - - - - - - - - - - - - - - -

_____

31
$$\begin{array}{r} 549 \\ -\ 45 \\ \hline \end{array}$$

594 ○ 584 ○ 504 ○ NH ○

STOP

LISTENING

PARENT PAGE

The text that appears in blue print is intended for an adult to read aloud.

Listen to these sentences as I read. Then find the word or words that best complete each sentence.

1. We don't want anything to *harm* our new puppy. To *harm* means to —
   help…heal…hurt.

2. If I *discover* some treasure, I will be rich. To *discover* something is to —
   hide it…find it…bury it.

3. Ava sat under a *clump* of trees. Another name for *clump* is —
   limp…bunch…shade.

4. Keesha *rescued* the baby bird from the cat. To *rescue* is to —
   save…wash…feed.

5. The color in my red shirt might *fade* in the wash. To *fade* is to —
   get lighter…get darker… get smaller.

6. Rodrigo gave Darla a birthday *gift*. Another name for *gift* is —
   box…present…cake.

7. We had to *pause* for a moment and rest. To *pause* is to —
   wait…sleep…hurry.

8. Kenji *aimed* the beanbag at the bucket. To *aim* is to —
   clap…mark…point.

9. Cheng fished in the *stream*. Another name for *stream* is —
   creek…sea…pond.

10. Dad *repaired* our toaster. To *repair* something is to —
    replace it…fix it…return it.

11. Her book is *below* the table. Another word for *below* is —
    over…above…under.

12. The sad story made us *weep*. To *weep* is to —
    yell…laugh…cry.

1 ○ help
   ○ heal
   ○ hurt

7 ○ wait
   ○ sleep
   ○ hurry

2 ○ hide it
   ○ find it
   ○ bury it

8 ○ clap
   ○ mark
   ○ point

3 ○ limp
   ○ bunch
   ○ shade

9 ○ creek
   ○ sea
   ○ pond

4 ○ save
   ○ wash
   ○ feed

10 ○ replace it
   ○ fix it
   ○ return it

5 ○ get lighter
   ○ get darker
   ○ get smaller

11 ○ over
   ○ above
   ○ under

6 ○ box
   ○ present
   ○ cake

12 ○ yell
   ○ laugh
   ○ cry

STOP

Listen to these stories as I read. Then find the picture that answers the question.

Every morning before school, Lila eats a good breakfast. After breakfast, she brushes her teeth. Next, she dresses and combs her hair. Then she is ready to walk to the bus stop.

1. What does Lila do after she eats breakfast?

_____

Mr. Stone's class put on a talent show. Each student did something to help with the show. Marcia and Tom made the scenery. Sam played the trumpet. Jody did a tap dance. Marty and Kim sang a song.

2. What did Sam play in the talent show?

3. What is something another student might do in the talent show?

_____

Mrs. Wallace owns her own bakery. She likes the smell of fresh baking.

4. Which picture shows something you could buy in Mrs. Wallace's store?

If I could, you know I would
Sail the ocean blue.
I'd have a big adventure,
And meet a pirate, too.

5. Which picture shows how the author of the poem could travel on the ocean?

_____

I am sharp. My job is to cut hair. I can also cut flowers or paper.

6. What am I?

_____

Ella made a Mother's Day card. She drew three roses in the middle. She drew a butterfly above the roses. Under the roses, she drew a bow. On top she wrote "To Mother."

7. Which card did Ella make?

_____

Juan and Maria like to help their father. When the leaves have fallen from the trees, it is time for the family to start working.

8. Which picture shows how Juan and Maria help their father in the fall?

1

2

3

4

5

6

7

TO MOTHER   TO MOTHER   TO MOTHER

8

STOP

Listen to these stories as I read. Then answer the questions.

Keiko just lost her tooth. She is happy it fell out. It had been loose for seven days. Now she can eat without feeling any pain.

1. When did Keiko lose her tooth?
   today…seven days ago…two weeks ago

2. How did Keiko feel about losing her tooth?
   glad…sad…mad

We saw a special parade at the zoo.
The animals lined up two by two!
The giraffes so tall,
The ferrets so small,
And the elephants, of course, were the
   biggest of all.

3. Why were the animals lined up?
   *It was raining….There was a parade….
   They were on their way to Africa.*

4. Which animals were tall?
   elephants…ferrets…giraffes

The word dinosaur means "terrible lizard." These creatures roamed Earth millions of years ago. Some were as small as chickens. Others were larger than elephants. We learn about dinosaurs from the things they left behind.

5. How small were some dinosaurs?
   *as small as bees…as small as teacups…
   as small as chickens*

6. How do we learn about dinosaurs?
   *from the things they left behind…from the people
   who were living then…from animals today*

- First, take the eggs, milk, and bread out of the refrigerator.
- Next, break the eggs into a bowl. Use a fork to mix them with the milk.
- Then put the bread in the bowl. Turn it over.
- Finally, cook the bread in a pan on the stove.
- When your French toast is ready, enjoy your breakfast!

7. What do these directions tell you how to make?
   biscuits…french toast…cereal

8. What should you do after you mix the milk and eggs in a bowl?
   *add the bread…put it on the stove…
   stir in some butter*

1 ○ today
○ seven days ago
○ two weeks ago

2 ○ glad
○ sad
○ mad

3 ○ It was raining.
○ There was a parade.
○ They were on their way to Africa.

4 ○ elephants
○ ferrets
○ giraffes

5 ○ as small as bees
○ as small as teacups
○ as small as chickens

6 ○ from the things they left behind
○ from the people who were living then
○ from animals today

7 ○ biscuits
○ French toast
○ cereal

8 ○ add the bread
○ put it on the stove
○ stir in some butter

STOP

Listen to these sentences as I read. Then find the word or words that best complete each sentence.

1. My uncle lives in a *cabin* at the lake.
A *cabin* is a —
shed…boat…small house.

2. José has to *prepare* for his part in the play.
To *prepare* is to —
calm down…leave…get ready.

3. Zoe saw a *bug* on a leaf. Another name for
bug is —
insect…igloo…pet.

4. This instrument makes a sound when you *strike*
it. To *strike* is to —
hit…smooth…clean.

5. Our family took a *vacation* to the Grand
Canyon. Another name for *vacation* is —
illness…trip…excuse.

6. Su Ling missed the beginning of class because
she was *tardy* this morning.
To be *tardy* is to be —
present…late…early.

7. I saw the movie the *day before today*. The *day
before today* is called —
tomorrow…tonight…yesterday.

8. My mom met a *pleasant* lady who gave us
directions. *Pleasant* means —
nice…rude…poor.

9. Katy found an *unusual* rock. If something is
unusual, it is — *not common…square…normal.*

10. The knight was *brave* when he fought the
dragon. *Brave* means —
not afraid…not angry…not smart.

11. The weather forecaster said clouds might *appear*
today. To *appear* is to —
go away…be seen…get faster.

12. We walked through the *woods* and saw many
animals and trees. Another word for *woods* is —
ocean…desert…forest.

1 ○ shed
   ○ boat
   ○ small house

2 ○ calm down
   ○ leave
   ○ get ready

3 ○ insect
   ○ igloo
   ○ pet

4 ○ hit
   ○ smooth
   ○ clean

5 ○ illness
   ○ trip
   ○ excuse

6 ○ present
   ○ late
   ○ early

7 ○ tomorrow
   ○ tonight
   ○ yesterday

8 ○ nice
   ○ rude
   ○ poor

9 ○ not common
   ○ square
   ○ normal

10 ○ not afraid
   ○ not angry
   ○ not smart

11 ○ go away
   ○ be seen
   ○ get faster

12 ○ ocean
   ○ desert
   ○ forest

GO ON

Listen to these stories as I read. Then find the picture that answers the question.

Fatima helped her aunt make a quilt. Fatima cut four squares and three circles from the cloth.

13. Which picture shows how Fatima cut the cloth?

_____

Miko turned on the water in the tub to take a bath. Then the telephone rang and Miko answered it. She talked to her friend for an hour and forgot about the water in the tub.

14. Which picture shows what probably happened next?

_____

Amy is learning a new dance. Her teacher tells her to put her arms down at her sides and stand with her feet apart.

15. Which picture shows how Amy should stand?

_____

Diego's grandmother gave him a box with a new pet in it. When Diego looked in the box, he saw long ears and a short, fluffy tail.

16. What pet did Diego receive?

_____

Mr. Sakata told his class, "This week you will choose a book from the school library to read. The book must tell a story. Then you will write a report about your book."

17. What is the *first* thing each student must do?

Mr. Jordan made a delicious strawberry pie. First, he picked the berries. Then he mixed the dough for the crust. Finally, he rolled the dough flat.

18. What did Mr. Jordan do after he picked the berries?

_____

No one had lived in the old house on Gulf Road for more than 10 years. It was very scary-looking. One night, Paul and his friend Steve visited the house. Just as they opened the front door, something small and furry brushed against their legs. The boys decided to explore the house some other day and they ran home.

19. Which picture shows the house on Gulf Road?

20. What probably brushed by the boys at the house?

_____

Alex baked muffins for the bake sale. He measured and mixed the ingredients. Then he poured the batter into a pan and put the pan into the oven.

21. Which baking pan did Alex use?

Listen to these stories as I read. Then answer the questions.

- First, take the kite out of the package.
- Second, insert the wooden pieces into the back of the kite.
- Next, attach the end of a ball of string to the center of the kite.
- Finally, make a kite's tail from pieces of cloth. Attach the tail to the kite.
- If you like, you can paint or decorate your kite.

22. You need to attach wooden pieces to the kite so that —
    the kite can fly…the kite won't blow away… you can decorate the kite.

23. To make the kite fly, you do not have to —
    attach some string…insert wooden pieces… paint the kite.

Rod helps out at his family's store every day. Before going to school, Rod sweeps the store. After school, Rod does his homework. Then he takes out the trash. When it is time to close the store, Rod makes sure all the lights are turned out.

24. Before school, Rod helps by —
    sweeping the store…taking out the trash… turning out all the lights.

25. Rod helps close the store by —
    doing his homework…taking out the trash…turning out all the lights.

There are many simple ways to save water. One is taking showers instead of baths. Showers use much less water and get you just as clean. You can also save water when you are washing your hands and brushing your teeth. Don't let the water run while you are soaping up your hands or brushing your teeth. Turn the water on just when you need it to rinse.

26. One thing that does not help save water is —
    taking a shower…catching rainwater…taking a bath.

27. When washing your hands, you should turn on the water only to —
    soap up your hands…rinse…take a bath.

"Oh, my goodness!" said Jake.
When he opened his backpack,
Out came a snake!

28. What came out of Jake's backpack?
    his frog…his snake…his homework

29. How did Jake feel when he saw it?
    surprised…tired…sad

Ms. Jackson's class did a science experiment. She divided the class into groups and gave each person a job. "In this group, Michiko will pass out the materials," Ms. Jackson said. "Jamal will be the recorder. Scott will be in charge of cleanup. Jenna will be the leader."

30. What was Ms. Jackson's class doing?
    practicing a play…running a race…doing a science experiment

31. Who will be the leader?
    Michiko…Jenna…Jamal

Mr. Diaz packed the gear for the camping trip. He packed the tent. He put food in a cooler. He packed lanterns, flashlights, and bug spray. At the campsite, the members of the family set up the tent. They cooked a meal over the fire. Only when it was time to go to bed did they discover that Mr. Diaz had forgotten to pack something.

32. What did Mr. Diaz probably forget to pack?
    sleeping bags…radio…flashlights

33. What is a good title for this story?
    "How to Go Camping"…"The Diaz Family's Problem"…"Fun with Flashlights"

22
- ◯ the kite can fly
- ◯ the kite won't blow away
- ◯ you can decorate the kite

23
- ◯ attach some string
- ◯ insert wooden pieces
- ◯ paint the kite

24
- ◯ sweeping the store
- ◯ taking out the trash
- ◯ turning out all the lights

25
- ◯ doing his homework
- ◯ taking out the trash
- ◯ turning out all the lights

26
- ◯ taking a shower
- ◯ catching rainwater
- ◯ taking a bath

27
- ◯ soap up your hands
- ◯ rinse
- ◯ take a bath

28
- ◯ his frog
- ◯ his snake
- ◯ his homework

29
- ◯ surprised
- ◯ tired
- ◯ sad

30
- ◯ practicing a play
- ◯ running a race
- ◯ doing a science experiment

31
- ◯ Michiko
- ◯ Jenna
- ◯ Jamal

32
- ◯ sleeping bags
- ◯ radio
- ◯ flashlights

33
- ◯ "How to Go Camping"
- ◯ "The Diaz Family's Problem"
- ◯ "Fun with Flashlights"

STOP

LANGUAGE

The text that appears in blue print is intended for an adult to read aloud.

Listen to the story. Then find the picture that answers the question.

It was Saturday and it was raining. Mei could not go out to play with her friends. After lunch, Mei told her mother, "I have nothing to do." Her mother asked, "Why don't you watch TV?" But Mei didn't want to watch TV. Then Mei's mother showed her a trunk filled with old clothes, purses, hats, and other things.

1. Which picture shows how Mei had fun on a rainy day?

Elena and Ricardo were helping their mother by setting the table. Elena placed the spoon and fork on either side of the plate. Ricardo crossed the spoon and fork and put them on the plate. Then the spoon cried, "That's not right!" and it jumped off the plate.

2. Which picture shows the part of the story that could not really happen?

My grandmother lives in the state of Maine.
When we go to visit her, we travel by ——.

3. Which picture shows something that will finish this rhyming poem?

Frankie's father gave him a box. When Frankie looked inside the box, he saw short ears and a wagging tail.

4. Which picture shows Frankie's new pet?

Mr. Henson was building a new birdhouse for his bird, Grover. First, he sawed the wood into pieces. Next, he nailed the pieces together. Finally, he painted Grover's new birdhouse.

5. What did Mr. Henson do first?

1

○   ○   ○

2

○   ○   ○

3

○   ○   ○

4

○   ○   ○

5

○   ○   ○

Read with me as I read this report. Then answer the questions.

Ramona wrote this report titled Getting Around in the City.

> Many people drive cars.
> In large cities.
> Some people ride in taxis.
> Some people ride the bus.

1. Which sentence in Ramona's report is not a complete sentence?
   Many people drive cars....In large cities....Some people ride in taxis....

_____

2. Choose the sentence that makes sense at the end of this paragraph.

> We live in the city.
> My father rides a bus to work.
> It is too far for him to walk.

   Which sentence will Ramona write next?

   A few people might walk to work....People work in a city....The city is noisy....

3. Look at the underlined words with the number 1 under them. Did Ramona use the right words? Should she write *We is living*, *We live*, or is the group of underlined words *correct the way it is*?

4. Look at the underlined words with the number 2 under them. Did Ramona use the right words? Should she write *My Father* (with both words capitalized), *my father* (with both words lowercased), or is the group of underlined words *correct the way it is*?

Getting Around in the City

Many people drive cars.
In large cities.
Some people ride in taxis.
Most people ride the bus.

1 ○ Many people drive cars.
   ○ In large cities.
   ○ Some people ride in taxis.

2 ○ A few people might walk to work.
   ○ People work in a city.
   ○ The city is noisy.

We lives in the city.
(1)
My father rides a bus to work.
(2)
It is too far for him to walk.

---

3   We is living   We live   Correct the way it is.
        ○   ○   ○

4   My Father   my father   Correct the way it is.
        ○   ○   ○

GO ON ➡

Listen to this information about Larry's report. Then answer the questions.

Larry's teacher asked the class to write a story about their pets. Larry has a horse. He decided to write about the tricks his horse can do.

5. Why is Larry writing a story? Is it *to tell how to teach a horse tricks, to tell why he loves horses,* or *to tell a story about his pet*?

_____

6. Larry wanted to use these words in his story: *kiss, tricks,* and *hand.* Fill in the circle under the word that would be listed first in a dictionary.

Read with me as I read the first part of Larry's report, titled My Smart Horse.

> My horse can do many tricks.
> He lifts his leg to my hand shake.
> He gives me a kiss with his nose.
> My horse can also play hiding games.

7. Look at the underlined sentence. Did Larry write this sentence correctly? Should he write *He lifts his leg to hand shake my, He lifts his leg to shake my hand,* or is the sentence *correct the way it is*?

_____

8. Larry wants to describe what his horse looks like. Should he write *My horse is brown and white, I like to see my horse run,* or *My horse comes when he sees me*?

5
- ○ to tell how to teach a horse tricks
- ○ to tell why he loves horses
- ○ to tell a story about his pet

6

kiss	tricks	hand
○	○	○

My Smart Horse

My horse can do many tricks.
He lifts his leg to my hand shake.
He gives me a kiss with his nose.
My horse can also play hiding games.

7
- ○ He lifts his leg to hand shake my.
- ○ He lifts his leg to shake my hand.
- ○ Correct the way it is.

8
- ○ My horse is brown and white.
- ○ I like to see my horse run.
- ○ My horse comes when he sees me.

GO ON ➡

Read with me as I read the next part of Larry's report.

> I gave my horse a treat after each trick.
> He likes carrots best.
> If I forget his treat, he shakes his head.

9. Look at the underlined word, *gived*, with the number 1 under it. Did Larry use the right word? Should he write *gave*, *give*, or is the word *correct the way it is*?

10. Look at the underlined word, *likes*, with the number 2 under it. Did Larry use the right word? Should he write *like*, *liked*, or is the word *correct the way it is*?

Now I will read to you about Vicki's class.

Vicki's class put together a report about how people travel from place to place. They put a table of contents at the front of the report. Read with me as I read the table of contents. Chapter 1 is called Over Tracks and begins on page 6. Chapter 2 is called Up in Air and begins on page 21. Chapter 3 is called On Land and begins on page 38. Chapter 4 is called By Water and begins on page 50.

11. Would an article about airplanes be in Chapter 1, 2, or 3?

12. Would you find information about ships on page 21, 38, or 50?

I gived my horse a treat after each trick.
(1)

He likes carrots best.
(2)

If I forget his treat, he shakes his head.

9   gave   give   Correct the way it is.
         ○   ○   ○

10   like   liked   Correct the way it is.
         ○   ○   ○

Table of Contents

1. Over Tracks ...page 6
2. Up in Air ....page 21
3. On Land ....page 38
4. By Water........page 50

11   1   2   3
         ○   ○   ○

12   21   38   50
         ○   ○   ○

STOP

Listen to these sentences. Three of the words will be listed. Find the word that is not spelled correctly.

1. I went along for the ride.

2. Did you see the cake I baked?

3. He was eating an apple.

4. Tony walked to the store by himself.

5. The two babies played quietly.

6. Alberto had a party at school today.

7. Please pass the milk.

8. I can cross the street now.

9. Those boys joined the baseball team.

10. The frog sat on the green grass.

11. It is Raul's turn to wash dishes.

12. Brian picked these flowers.

1 ○ wint
  ○ along
  ○ ride

2 ○ you
  ○ see
  ○ bakt

3 ○ wus
  ○ eating
  ○ apple

4 ○ walkt
  ○ store
  ○ himself

5 ○ two
  ○ babies
  ○ playd

6 ○ had
  ○ party
  ○ skool

7 ○ Pleaze
  ○ pass
  ○ milk

8 ○ can
  ○ cros
  ○ street

9 ○ boyes
  ○ joined
  ○ team

10 ○ frog
   ○ gren
   ○ grass

11 ○ turn
   ○ wash
   ○ dishs

12 ○ pickd
   ○ these
   ○ flowers

Listen to these stories I read. Then answer the questions.

The house on Edmond Street has a pointed roof. The chimney is crooked.

1. Which picture shows the house on Edmond Street?

Inez and Isabella are twins. Even though they look alike, they are very different. They like to do different things. They wear their hair the same way, but they always dress differently.

2. Which picture shows Inez and Isabella?

Chris and his family went to the lake. They saw a family of bears swimming across the lake. Then the bears joined Chris and his family at the picnic table for lunch. Later, Chris offered to clean up the mess at the picnic table.

3. Which picture shows something that could not really happen?

While we were walking by the lake,
We saw a black and yellow ——.

4. Which picture shows something that will finish this rhyming poem?

Gloria was very busy on Saturday. She made her bed and then washed the dishes. When she was done, she went to her room to do her homework.

5. Which picture shows what Gloria did first?

1

2

3

4

5

GO ON

Listen as I tell you about Pat's science project.

Pat is going to make a project for the science fair. She is going to tell how seeds move from place to place.

6. What should Pat do before writing her science report? Should she *list ways seeds move, plant some seeds*, or *glue seeds to paper*?

_____

7. What should Pat do to find more information about how seeds move? Should she *buy seeds from a store, find a library book about seeds*, or *go to a park*?

Read with me as I read the first part of Pat's report, titled Animals Move Seeds.

> Some animals move seeds.
> Birds pick up seeds to eat.
> They may dropping the seeds as they fly.
> I have a new dog.
> The seeds grow where they fall on the ground.

8. Look at the underlined word, *dropping*, in the first part of Pat's report. Did she use the right word? Should she write *drops, drop*, or is the word *correct the way it is*?

_____

9. Which sentence does not belong in this report? Is it *Some animals move seeds, Birds pick up seeds to eat*, or *I have a new dog*?

6   ○ list ways seeds move
        ○ plant some seeds
        ○ glue seeds to paper

7   ○ buy seeds from a store
        ○ find a library book about seeds
        ○ go to a park

Animals Move Seeds

Some animals move seeds.
Birds pick up seeds to eat.
They may <u>dropping</u> the seeds as they fly.
I have a new dog.
The seeds grow where they fall on the ground.

---

8   ○ drops
        ○ drop
        ○ Correct the way it is.

9   ○ Some animals move seeds.
        ○ Birds pick up seeds to eat.
        ○ I have a new dog.

GO ON ➡

Read with me as I read the next part of Pat's report.

> Some seeds stick to the fur of animals.
> They dont fall off easily.
> The ends of the seeds are turned up.

10. Look at the underlined word, *dont*. Did Pat use the right word? Should she write *don't* (with the apostrophe between the *n* and the *t*), *do'nt* (with the apostrophe between the *o* and the *n*), or is the word *correct the way it is?*

_____

11. Pat wants to describe what the seeds look like. Should she write *The seed ends look sharp and look like a fishhook*, *The seed ends look sharp and like a fishhook*, or *The seed ends look like a sharp fishhook*

_____

12. Pat used these words in her report: *stick*, *seeds*, and *sharp*. Which word would be listed first in the dictionary?

Some seeds stick to the fur of animals.
They <u>dont</u> fall off easily.
The ends of the seeds are turned up.

10
○ don't
○ do'nt
○ Correct the way it is.

11
○ The seed ends look sharp and look like a fishhook.
○ The seed ends look sharp and like a fishhook.
○ The seed ends look like a sharp fishhook.

12
stick   seeds   sharp
○   ○   ○

GO ON ➡

Listen to these sentences. Three of the words will be listed. Find the word that is not spelled correctly.

13. The play was over at four o'clock.

14. The pretty pink present is for Ida.

15. Liz told a funny story.

16. This is the end of the line.

17. The boys splashed in the water.

18. Max bought two brushes.

19. I didn't mean what I said.

20. The pond is filled with fish.

21. Your face has dirt on it.

22. Put your toys away in your room.

23. Mother parked close to the store.

24. The snake lives under the rock.

13 ○ play
   ○ overe
   ○ four

14 ○ prety
   ○ pink
   ○ present

15 ○ told
   ○ funny
   ○ storie

16 ○ This
   ○ ende
   ○ line

17 ○ boys
   ○ splashd
   ○ water

18 ○ bought
   ○ two
   ○ brushs

19 ○ mean
   ○ what
   ○ sed

20 ○ pond
   ○ filld
   ○ fish

21 ○ fase
   ○ has
   ○ dirt

22 ○ put
   ○ toyes
   ○ room

23 ○ Mother
   ○ parkt
   ○ close

24 ○ livz
   ○ under
   ○ rock

STOP

PRACTICE TEST 1: WORD STUDY SKILLS

PARENT PAGE

The text that appears in blue print is intended for an adult to read aloud.

Listen to the word. Find the word that begins with the same sound.

1. *Soup*
   What word begins with the sound you hear at the beginning of the word *soup*?

   _____

2. *Doll*
   What word begins with the sound you hear at the beginning of the word *doll*?

   _____

3. *Bottle*
   What word begins with the sound you hear at the beginning of the word *bottle*?

   _____

4. *Happy*
   What word begins with the sound you hear at the beginning of the word *happy*?

   _____

5. *Toast*
   What word begins with the sound you hear at the beginning of the word *toast*?

   _____

6. *Friend*
   What word begins with the sound you hear at the beginning of the word *friend*?

7. *Wish*
   What word begins with the sound you hear at the beginning of the word *wish*?

   _____

8. *Kitten*
   What word begins with the sound you hear at the beginning of the word *kitten*?

   _____

9. *Purple*
   What word begins with the sound you hear at the beginning of the word *purple*?

   _____

10. *Ship*
    What word begins with the sound you hear at the beginning of the word *ship*?

    _____

11. *Rabbit*
    What word begins with the sound you hear at the beginning of the word *rabbit*?

    _____

12. *Grasshopper*
    What word begins with the sound you hear at the beginning of the word *grasshopper*?

1   sip   tip   plate
    ◯   ◯   ◯

7   fit   mats   wet
    ◯   ◯   ◯

2   gate   dig   puppy
    ◯   ◯   ◯

8   cake   sat   take
    ◯   ◯   ◯

3   tub   eat   bite
    ◯   ◯   ◯

9   rip   ear   pen
    ◯   ◯   ◯

4   hot   not   cot
    ◯   ◯   ◯

10   shell   tell   well
     ◯   ◯   ◯

5   most   sun   teeth
    ◯   ◯   ◯

11   bear   air   run
     ◯   ◯   ◯

6   pin   frog   barn
    ◯   ◯   ◯

12   hill   green   four
     ◯   ◯   ◯

GO ON ➡

Listen to the word. Find the word that ends with the same sound.

13. *Bat*
    What word ends with the sound you hear at the end of the word *bat*?

_____

14. *Rip*
    What word ends with the sound you hear at the end of the word *rip*?

_____

15. *Toss*
    What word ends with the sound you hear at the end of the word *toss*?

_____

16. *Mad*
    What word ends with the sound you hear at the end of the word *mad*?

_____

17. *Wagon*
    What word ends with the sound you hear at the end of the word *wagon*?

_____

18. *Trick*
    What word ends with the sound you hear at the end of the word *trick*?

19. *Shirt*
    What word ends with the sound you hear at the end of the word *shirt*?

_____

20. *Fox*
    What word ends with the sound you hear at the end of the word *fox*?

_____

21. *Last*
    What word ends with the sound you hear at the end of the word *last*?

_____

22. *Butter*
    What word ends with the sound you hear at the end of the word *butter*?

_____

23. *Swim*
    What word ends with the sound you hear at the end of the word *swim*?

_____

24. *Wonderful*
    What word ends with the sound you hear at the end of the word *wonderful*?

13	cut ○	cup ○	car ○

14	tub ○	tan ○	tap ○

15	mop ○	mix ○	mess ○

16	kick ○	kid ○	kitten ○

17	head ○	hot ○	hen ○

18	duck ○	trip ○	rice ○

19	hop ○	hum ○	hurt ○

20	wax ○	wig ○	won ○

21	ten ○	test ○	tree ○

22	family ○	fast ○	father ○

23	west ○	name ○	sweet ○

24	belt ○	bee ○	bell ○

GO ON ➡

Read these directions aloud to your child.

Look at the picture. Find the word that names the picture.

25

ball ○   bell ○   bill ○

26

hands ○   ants ○   arts ○

27

bowl ○   boy ○   box ○

28

plane ○   plant ○   play ○

29

care ○   cake ○   cave ○

30

prince ○   pen ○   pond ○

31

cry ○   crayon ○   creep ○

32

sloppy ○   slide ○   sled ○

GO ON ➡

Listen to the word. Find the word that rhymes.

33. *Feet*
What word rhymes with *feet*?
_____

34. *Play*
What word rhymes with *play*?
_____

35. *House*
What word rhymes with *house*?
_____

36. *Pie*
What word rhymes with *pie*?
_____

37. *Barn*
What word rhymes with *barn*?
_____

38. *Silly*
What word rhymes with *silly*?

39. *Moon*
What word rhymes with *moon*?
_____

40. *Brush*
What word rhymes with *brush*?
_____

41. *Night*
What word rhymes with *night*?
_____

42. *Park*
What word rhymes with *park*?
_____

43. *True*
What word rhymes with *true*?
_____

44. *Clocks*
What word rhymes with *clocks*?

33	hoot ○	hot ○	heat ○	39	nut ○	noon ○	new ○
34	day ○	date ○	dark ○	40	rash ○	rich ○	rush ○
35	mows ○	moon ○	mouse ○	41	kite ○	kit ○	cat ○
36	fly ○	flower ○	fork ○	42	shark ○	sheep ○	shoe ○
37	yarn ○	bear ○	here ○	43	nap ○	now ○	new ○
38	sleepy ○	hilly ○	happy ○	44	bows ○	balls ○	box ○

STOP

PRACTICE TEST 2:
READING COMPREHENSION

PARENT PAGE

The text that appears in blue print is intended for an adult to read aloud.

Read these riddles with me. Find the picture that shows what the sentences tell about.

1. You can climb it.
   It is made of wood.

2. I have four legs.
   I cannot walk or run.

3. I have stripes.
   I can growl.

4. You can rock on it.
   It is a toy.

5. It is found in space.
   It can fly.

6. I am big.
   I have fur.

7. It has strings.
   It makes music.

8. It can float.
   It can swim.

1 You can climb it.
   It is made of wood.

   ○   ○   ○

5 It is found in space.
   It can fly.

   ○   ○   ○

2 I have four legs.
   I cannot walk or run.

   ○   ○   ○

6 I am big.
   I have fur.

   ○   ○   ○

3 I have stripes.
   I can growl.

   ○   ○   ○

7 It has strings.
   It makes music.

   ○   ○   ○

4 You can rock on it.
   It is a toy.

   ○   ○   ○

8 It can float.
   It can swim.

   ○   ○   ○

GO ON ➡

Look at the picture. Then read these sentences with me. Find the word that best completes the sentence.

9. Gino is riding his big brother's —

10. Gino splashed water on Ms. Zamora's —

11. Aunt Abby is feeding her —

12. The baby is drinking from a —

13. The children are in a —

14. They listen to —

15. Eileen is holding a —

16. She caught a —

17. Eileen is —

9 Gino is riding his big brother's

tricycle   bicycle   wagon
○   ○   ○

10 Gino splashed water on Ms. Zamora's

dress   hat   car
○   ○   ○

11 Aunt Abby is feeding her

puppy   baby   self
○   ○   ○

12 The baby is drinking from a

cup   bottle   straw
○   ○   ○

13 The children are in a

classroom   store   mall
○   ○   ○

14 They listen to

a farmer   an artist   a teacher
○   ○   ○

15 Eileen is holding a

stick   fishing pole   broom
○   ○   ○

16 She caught a

cold   rabbit   fish
○   ○   ○

17 Eileen is

jumping   frowning   smiling
○   ○   ○

Read this story with me. Then answer the questions about the story.

Interesting Insects

Caterpillars and butterflies are interesting insects. They live in many places in the world. They live in cool places. They live in hot places.

Caterpillars are born in the early spring. They eat for many months. Then they become butterflies.

There are many kinds of butterflies. Some butterflies live only for a few weeks. Other butterflies live for several months. Some butterflies are brown and green. They can hide in the trees. Other butterflies have bright colors. All these butterflies help make a colorful world.

18. Where do caterpillars and butterflies live?

    only in hot places

    only in cold places

    in many places in the world

19. From this story you know that

    caterpillars eat very little.

    all butterflies live a long time.

    there are many different kinds of butterflies.

20. When do caterpillars become butterflies?

    in early spring

    after eating for many months

    after several years

21. Why can some butterflies hide in trees?

    Their colors are the same as the colors of a tree.

    They have very bright colors.

    They are very small.

Interesting Insects

Caterpillars and butterflies are interesting insects. They live in many places in the world. They live in cool places. They live in hot places.

Caterpillars are born in the early spring. They eat for many months. Then they become butterflies.

There are many kinds of butterflies. Some butterflies live only for a few weeks. Other butterflies live for several months. Some butterflies are brown and green. They can hide in the trees. Other butterflies have bright colors. All these butterflies help make a colorful world.

18 Where do caterpillars and butterflies live?

   ○ only in hot places

   ○ only in cold places

   ○ in many places in the world

19 From this story you know that

   ○ caterpillars eat very little.

   ○ all butterflies live a long time.

   ○ there are many different kinds of butterflies.

20 When do caterpillars become butterflies?

   ○ in early spring

   ○ after eating for many months

   ○ after several years

21 Why can some butterflies hide in trees?

   ○ Their colors are the same as the colors of a tree.

   ○ They have very bright colors.

   ○ They are very small.

GO ON ➡

Read this story with me. Then answer the questions about the story.

A Day of Fun

Kim went to the circus. She saw many things. There were three dancing bears. One of them wore a skirt. She also saw an elephant walk on its back legs.

Kim saw a tall clown in a little car. She laughed when the clown got stuck.

Kim looked up to watch people walking on wires. She sat very still. She was afraid they would fall. Kim wants to visit the circus again.

22. This story tells about

    Kim's dog.

    how to be a clown.

    a trip to the circus.

23. On how many legs did the elephant walk?

    Write your answer on the lines.

24. Why did Kim laugh?

    She thought the clown was funny.

    She thought the people on wires were funny.

    She told a joke.

25. You can tell that Kim

    didn't like the circus.

    wants to go to the zoo.

    enjoyed the circus.

A Day of Fun

Kim went to the circus. She saw many things. There were three dancing bears. One of them wore a skirt. She also saw an elephant walk on its back legs.

Kim saw a tall clown in a little car. She laughed when the clown got stuck.

Kim looked up to watch people walking on wires. She sat very still. She was afraid they would fall. Kim wants to visit the circus again.

22 **This story tells about**
- ○ Kim's dog.
- ○ how to be a clown.
- ○ a trip to the circus.

23 **On how many legs did the elephant walk?**

_____

- - - - - - - - - - - - - - - - - - - -

_____

24 **Why did Kim laugh?**
- ○ She thought the clown was funny.
- ○ She thought the people on wires were funny.
- ○ She told a joke.

25 **You can tell that Kim**
- ○ didn't like the circus.
- ○ wants to go to the zoo.
- ○ enjoyed the circus.

STOP

PRACTICE TEST 3:
MATH PROBLEM SOLVING

PARENT PAGE

The text that appears in blue print is intended for an adult to read aloud.

1. Which picture can be folded on the dotted line so that the parts on each side of the line match exactly?

2. How many marbles are there altogether in this picture?

3. Which number shows *three hundred fifteen?*

4. Which box has the most hearts?

5. Which number tells how many blocks there are altogether?

6. Which bird is the fourth bird from the cage?

1

○　○　○　○

2

32　23　21　3
○　○　○　○

3

315　350　3015　153
○　○　○　○

4

○　○　○　○

5

6　106　56　66
○　○　○　○

6

○　　○　○　　○

GO ON ➡

7. Which number means fifty plus eight?

_____

8. Which number is 10 less than the number on the gift?

_____

9. Which number sentence is in the same fact family as the number sentence in the box?

_____

10. What number goes in the box to make this number sentence correct? Write the number on the lines.

_____

11. Which of these numbers is more than 45 and less than 69?

_____

12. Which two numbers have a seven in the ones place?

7

| 50 + 8 | 85 ○ | 508 ○ | 58 ○ | 580 ○ |

8

42

| 32 ○ | 52 ○ | 41 ○ | 24 ○ |

9

5 + 1 = 6

| 6 + 5 = 11 ○ | 6 − 5 = 1 ○ | 5 − 1 = 4 ○ | 6 + 1 = 7 ○ |

10

8 + 0 = ☐

_____

– – – – – – – – – – – – – – –

_____

11

45 ☐ 69

| 81 ○ | 38 ○ | 73 ○ | 52 ○ |

12

| 71, 72 ○ | 27, 17 ○ | 71, 17 ○ | 71, 67 ○ |

GO ON ➡

13. Which numbers mean the same as *three plus four*?

_____

14. Which shape has one of its six parts shaded?

_____

15. Which square is divided into four equal parts?

_____

16. Which picture shows one of the three apples eaten?

_____

17. Look at the graph. How many boxes of flower seeds were sold?

13

$3 + 4$ $4 - 3$ $7 + 3$ $7 - 4$ $4 + 3$

                    ◯   ◯   ◯   ◯

14

◯   ◯   ◯   ◯

15

◯   ◯   ◯   ◯

16

◯   ◯   ◯   ◯

17

BOXES OF SEEDS SOLD	
Flower Seeds	🌸🌸🌸🌸🌸
Vegetable Seeds	🥕🥕🥕🥕
Herb Seeds	🌿🌿🌿
Birdseed	🐦🐦

         2   3   4   5

         ◯   ◯   ◯   ◯

GO ON ➡

18. Maria lives in apartment number 22. The doors are in order. Which door shows Maria's apartment?

19. Look at the tally chart. How many crayons does Monica have in her school box? Write the number on the lines.

20. Look for a pattern. Which piece of fruit comes next in this pattern?

21. Look at the figure on the left. Which figure on the right is exactly the same?

22. Which picture shows a triangle inside a square?

23. Yukio plays a game with paper shapes. She put eight diamonds, two squares, one triangle, and four circles into a box. If she picks a shape without looking, which shape will Yukio most likely pick?

18

19

School Box

✏️	IIII
🖍️	~~IIII~~ III
(eraser)	I
(glue)	II

20

🍎 ♡ 🍌 ♡ 🍇 ♡ ___

♡   🍇   🍎   🍌

○   ○   ○   ○

21

○   ○   ○   ○

22

○   ○   ○   ○

23

○   ○   ○   ○

GO ON ➡

24. Which number tells about how many fish long the aquarium is?

_____

25. Jay is measuring flour to make cookies. What measurement should Jay use to measure the flour?

_____

26. Chandra has piano lessons every Saturday at the time shown on the clock. Which of the numbers tells the time when Chandra has piano lessons?

_____

27. I am thinking of a number that is between 41 and 60. It has a 5 in it. Which of these numbers am I thinking of?

_____

28. I am thinking of a number that is less than 22. You say its name when you count by twos. It has an 8 in it. Which of these numbers am I thinking of?

24

9 ○   2 ○   4 ○   6 ○

25

miles ○   inches ○   cups ○   gallons ○

26

9:30 ○   3:30 ○   4:30 ○   4:00 ○

27

15 ○   42 ○   54 ○   65 ○

28

28 ○   18 ○   14 ○   11 ○

STOP

PARENT PAGE

The text that appears in blue print is intended for an adult to read aloud.

The answer choice NH means that the answer is not here.

1. Jason collects leaves. Yesterday he went hiking through the woods near the lake. He found five oak leaves. Then he found eight maple leaves. How many leaves did he find altogether?

2. Write the number that goes in the box to make the number sentence true. Add nine plus two.

3. Ellen likes rag dolls. She has seven rag dolls. For her birthday, she received three more rag dolls. How many rag dolls does Ellen have altogether?

4. The pet store is having a fish sale. There are 20 fish in one tank. There are 15 fish in another tank. How many fish are there in all?

1

5   8

14	13	12	NH
○	○	○	○

2

$$9 + 2 = \square$$

_____

- -

_____

3

7   3

4	10	13	NH
○	○	○	○

4

20   15

5	25	35	NH
○	○	○	○

GO ON ➤

109

5. Rita checked out 7 books from the library. She returned 4 of the books the next Saturday. How many library books does she still have?

6. Chi-Hun went to the airport. He saw 16 airplanes. He saw 6 helicopters. How many more airplanes than helicopters did he see?

7. There are 37 balls in the gym. Coach Ellis uses 4 balls for a game. How many balls are left?

8. Ms. Todd bought a package of 50 dinosaur stickers. She gave away 30 of the stickers to students in her class. How many dinosaur stickers does she have left?

5

7   4

_____

- - - - - - - - - - - - - - - - - - - -

_____

6

16   6

22   10   8   NH
○   ○   ○   ○

7

37   4

41   3   33   NH
○   ○   ○   ○

8

50   30

20   40   80   NH
○   ○   ○   ○

GO ON ➡

9
4 + 3 = ☐

1   6   8   NH
○   ○   ○   ○

10
$$\begin{array}{r} 5 \\ + 5 \\ \hline \end{array}$$

11
$$\begin{array}{r} 9 \\ + 6 \\ \hline \end{array}$$

16   15   3   NH
○   ○   ○   ○

12
$$\begin{array}{r} 4 \\ 2 \\ + 3 \\ \hline \end{array}$$

8   7   6   NH
○   ○   ○   ○

13
$$\begin{array}{r} 53 \\ + 2 \\ \hline \end{array}$$

55   59   61   NH
○   ○   ○   ○

14
$$\begin{array}{r} 83 \\ + 6 \\ \hline \end{array}$$

99   89   77   NH
○   ○   ○   ○

15
$$\begin{array}{r} 62 \\ + 10 \\ \hline \end{array}$$

82   80   72   NH
○   ○   ○   ○

16
$$\begin{array}{r} 27 \\ + 21 \\ \hline \end{array}$$

48   46   6   NH
○   ○   ○   ○

17
$$\begin{array}{r} 9 \\ 4 \\ + 5 \\ \hline \end{array}$$

16   17   18   NH
○   ○   ○   ○

18
$$\begin{array}{r} 66 \\ + 22 \\ \hline \end{array}$$

GO ON →

19   8 − 7 = ☐

   0   1   15   NH
   ○   ○   ○   ○

---

20   13 − 6 = ☐

   7   8   28   NH
   ○   ○   ○   ○

21
$$\begin{array}{r} 14 \\ -\ 7 \\ \hline \end{array}$$

   7   8   21   NH
   ○   ○   ○   ○

22
$$\begin{array}{r} 45 \\ -\ 4 \\ \hline \end{array}$$

23
$$\begin{array}{r} 98 \\ -\ 3 \\ \hline \end{array}$$

  96   94   65   NH
  ○   ○   ○   ○

24
$$\begin{array}{r} 62 \\ -\ 51 \\ \hline \end{array}$$

 113   13   11   NH
  ○   ○   ○   ○

25
$$\begin{array}{r} 70 \\ -\ 20 \\ \hline \end{array}$$

---

26   25 − 6 = ☐

  31   19   18   NH
  ○   ○   ○   ○

27
$$\begin{array}{r} 17 \\ -\ 8 \\ \hline \end{array}$$

  25   19   9   NH
  ○   ○   ○   ○

28
$$\begin{array}{r} 328 \\ -\ 18 \\ \hline \end{array}$$

 300   310   318   NH
  ○   ○   ○   ○

STOP

PARENT PAGE

The text that appears in blue print is intended for an adult to read aloud.

Listen to these sentences as I read. Then find the word or words that best complete each sentence.

1. The part of your body that you use to think is your —

   forehead…brain…heart.

2. My dog's tricks might amaze you. To *amaze* is to —

   surprise…upset…scare.

3. When Grandpa rescued a baby, he was called a hero. A *hero* is someone who does something —

   brave…easy…quickly.

4. After drinking a bowl of milk, the kitten was content. Another word for *content* is —

   happy…worried…funny.

5. It is Fred's turn to raise the flag. To *raise* is to —

   bring down…lift…fold.

6. Lee's sister has a cold, but Lee is not ill. Another word for *ill* is —

   lazy…sick…absent.

7. We sat at the back of the bus. Another name for the *back* is the —

   front…rear…middle.

8. Uncle Jeff will manage the new store. To *manage* is to —

   take care of…leave…talk about.

9. He made a sketch of the town. A *sketch* is a —

   song…book…drawing.

10. This is where we switch trains. To *switch* is to —

    change…tear…count.

11. The clown told a foolish joke. Another word for *foolish* is —

    excited…angry…silly.

12. Santos is waiting for us where two streets meet. A place where two streets meet is called —

    an avenue…a corner…a road.

13. Tia had to run quickly to get her books. To *run quickly* is to —

    dash…wander…slide.

1 ○ forehead
   ○ brain
   ○ heart

2 ○ surprise
   ○ upset
   ○ scare

3 ○ brave
   ○ easy
   ○ quickly

4 ○ happy
   ○ worried
   ○ funny

5 ○ bring down
   ○ lift
   ○ fold

6 ○ lazy
   ○ sick
   ○ absent

7 ○ front
   ○ rear
   ○ middle

8 ○ take care of
   ○ leave
   ○ talk about

9 ○ song
   ○ book
   ○ drawing

10 ○ change
   ○ tear
   ○ count

11 ○ excited
   ○ angry
   ○ silly

12 ○ an avenue
   ○ a corner
   ○ a road

13 ○ dash
   ○ wander
   ○ slide

GO ON➡

Listen to these sentences as I read. Then find the picture that answers the question.

Some animals have fur. Some animals have feathers.

14. Which of these animals does not have fur or feathers?

When Juan got home from school, he played with his dog, Scooter. They played until almost dark, when Juan's mother told him that it was time to come in and give Scooter his dinner.

15. Which picture shows how Juan gave Scooter his dinner?

Ryan's mother came home from the hospital with his baby sister, Christine. Ryan carried the suitcase into the house. Then Ryan helped wash the baby. Then Ryan's mother told him that he could feed Christine. He sat in the rocking chair and gave Christine her bottle.

16. What did Ryan do first?

17. Which picture shows how Ryan fed the baby?

Anita and her family went camping. They decided to swim in the lake before lunch. They put their lunch basket on the picnic table. Anita and her family did not know that a mother bear and her cubs were nearby.

18. Which picture shows what Anita and her family found when they returned to the picnic table?

Olivia and her mother went shopping. Olivia found a rack of hats and tried some on. Her mother laughed when Olivia tried on a hat that was so big it covered her eyes. When Olivia and her mother got home, it looked as if it might rain. "Please get my purse, Olivia, and take it into the house," said her mother. "And please make sure that rain can't get into the car."

19. Which picture shows what Olivia looked like when her mother laughed?

Animals have different things that they use to protect themselves. Some, like deer and goats, have horns. Others have sharp teeth.

20. Which picture shows something else animals might use to protect themselves?

Every weekend in the fall, Andrew has three jobs he has to do before he can play. First, he waters his mother's plants. Next, he washes the dishes. Then he helps his dad by raking the leaves in the yard. Now Andrew can go out and play.

21. What is the first thing Andrew does?

Today is Gina's seventh birthday. Her aunt gave her a pair of dancing shoes. Her uncle made her a dollhouse. Her stepfather also gave her a wonderful present—a fluffy white poodle named Snowball.

22. What did Gina's aunt give her for her birthday?

14

15

16

17

18

19

20

21

22

GO ON ➡

Listen to these stories as I read. Then answer the questions.

Patrick and his mother had just stepped out of their car when a heavy rain began to pour down. "Stand under the awning," Patrick's mother said. "I have to get something from the car so we won't get wet."

23. Patrick's mother went to the car to get —
   a flag…an umbrella…a sandwich.

Everyone enjoys the Plum Creek Library. In the mornings, retired people meet there to discuss books they have read. During the afternoons, young children check out books, listen to stories, and see puppet plays. In the evenings, students come there to study and do research.

24. Retired people meet at the library to —
   discuss books…play softball…put on puppet plays.

25. Students use the library to do research and —
   sleep…cook…study.

The Warners live in Chicago. They are going on a trip. First, they will drive to the airport. Then they will fly in a plane to Seattle. From there they will sail on a boat to Alaska. In Alaska, they will take a train to see different parts of the state.

26. The Warners are going on a trip to —
   California…Hawaii…Alaska.

27. The first thing they will do is —
   sail on a boat…ride in a car…fly in a plane.

Rolanda loves to visit her grandparents in Mexico. She goes there with her parents every summer. She sees all her aunts and uncles and cousins. When Rolanda and her family arrive, there is a big celebration. Then over the next few weeks, the family goes to parks, museums, and restaurants. Rolanda's favorite part is listening to her grandparents tell stories about the family. When it is time to go home, Rolanda is sad. But she knows that she'll be going back next year.

28. There is a big celebration because Rolanda and her family —
   come to visit…are leaving…have a birthday.

29. A good name for this story would be —
   "Rolanda and Her Aunts"…"Celebrations in Mexico"…"Rolanda's Trips to Mexico"

Jerome told Larry that Jerome's turtle could beat Larry's dog in a race. Larry didn't believe him, so they decided to see what would happen. The dog ran very fast, and the turtle crawled very slowly. But just before the dog reached the finish line, he saw another dog and ran off to play with it. The turtle kept crawling until he reached the finish line.

30. The dog didn't finish the race because he
   became tired…stumbled and fell…ran off to play.

Wesley and Beth were building a snow friend. First, they made three balls of snow. Then they stacked up the snowballs. They found two sticks for arms. They made a face with a carrot nose and raisin eyes and mouth. They put a cowboy hat on top of their snow friend's head. "I guess we can call it a snow cowpoke," said Beth.

31. Beth and Wesley are playing in the —
   sand…snow…dirt.

32. Wesley and Beth called their snow friend a cowpoke because of its —
   hat…nose…arms.

33. After building their snow friend, Beth and Wesley probably felt —
   afraid…proud…angry.

Robin's aunt and uncle took her to a theme park. The first thing Robin wanted to do was see the princess's castle. Then they rode on several rides. Robin's favorite ride went underwater. Cartoon characters waved at them as they walked around the park. The first day ended with a big parade and fireworks. As they walked to their hotel, Robin thanked her aunt and uncle for the wonderful gift.

34. The wonderful gift Robin's aunt and uncle gave her was a —
   trip to the theme park…gold bracelet…new sweater.

35. The first thing Robin wanted to see was the —
   cartoon characters…underwater ride… princess's castle.

36. The cartoon characters in the park —
   took Robin on a ride…waved at Robin… showed Robin a castle.

23 ○ a flag
   ○ an umbrella
   ○ a sandwich

24 ○ discuss books
   ○ play softball
   ○ put on puppet plays

25 ○ sleep
   ○ cook
   ○ study

26 ○ California
   ○ Hawaii
   ○ Alaska

27 ○ sail on a boat
   ○ ride in a car
   ○ fly in a plane

28 ○ come to visit
   ○ are leaving
   ○ have a birthday

29 ○ "Rolanda and Her Aunts"
   ○ "Celebrations in Mexico"
   ○ "Rolanda's Trips to Mexico"

30 ○ became tired
   ○ stumbled and fell
   ○ ran off to play

31 ○ sand
   ○ snow
   ○ dirt

32 ○ hat
   ○ nose
   ○ arms

33 ○ afraid
   ○ proud
   ○ angry

34 ○ trip to the theme park
   ○ gold bracelet
   ○ new sweater

35 ○ cartoon characters
   ○ underwater ride
   ○ princess's castle

36 ○ took Robin on a ride
   ○ waved at Robin
   ○ showed Robin a castle

STOP

PARENT PAGE

The text that appears in blue print is intended for an adult to read aloud.

Listen to these stories as I read. Then answer the questions.

Forest Lane is an old country road. There is a covered bridge on Forest Lane that is only wide enough for one car to drive across at a time.

1. Which picture shows Forest Lane?

Every morning before school, Lita eats a good breakfast. After breakfast, she always brushes her teeth. Next, she dresses and combs her hair. Then she is ready to walk to the school bus stop.

2. What is the first thing Lita does in the morning?

Rudy the goldfish lives in a fishbowl. Once Rudy lived in a sparkling stream in the woods. There he liked to hang in the trees near the stream.

3. Which picture shows something that could not really happen?

Sam and Rolando were walking in the woods one night. As they passed under a tree, Rolando felt something sticky on his face. He wiped his face to get it off.

4. What did Rolando feel on his face?

We looked all around for Richard's toy bear.
We finally found it behind a —.

5. Which picture shows something that will finish this rhyming poem?

1

2

3

4

5

GO ON ➡

Listen as I tell you about Matt's pool party.

Matt is having a pool party at his house. He is sending invitations to his friends.

6. Matt used these words in his invitation: *when…wish…water.*
   Which of these words would come first in a dictionary?

7. What information will Matt *not* put in his invitation?

   the time the party begins

   the size of the pool

   his house number and street name

Read with me as I read Matt's invitation.

> Dear Sam,
> I am having a pool party.
> It will be this Friday, August 19.
> Come to my house at 359 Pine Road.
> We will much fun have.

8. Look at the words with the number 1 under them. Did Matt use the right words? Should he write

   friday, august 19 (with *August* lowercased), *friday, August 19* (with *August* capitalized), or is it *correct the way it is*?

9. Look at the sentence with the number 2 under it. Did Matt use the right words? Should he write

   We will have much fun, We will have fun much, or is it *correct the way it is*?

6 when ○   wish ○   water ○

7
- ○ the time the party begins
- ○ the size of the pool
- ○ his house number and street name

> Dear Sam,
>
> I am having a pool party.
> It will be this Friday, August 19.
>   (1)
> Come to my house at 359 Pine Road.
> We will much fun have.
>   (2)

---

8 friday, august 19 ○   friday, August 19 ○   Correct the way it is. ○

9
- ○ We will have much fun.
- ○ We will have fun much.
- ○ Correct the way it is.

GO ON ➡

Listen to these sentences. Three of the words will be listed. Find the word that is not spelled correctly.

10. Mr. Jones read two stories to the class.

_____

11. The teacher called your name.

_____

12. Please give her a turn.

_____

13. Rosa was careful not to wake her father.

_____

14. My friend is riding his bike.

_____

15. Please pick up your toys before you leave.

16. Maria fell and bumped her nose.

_____

17. The girl made three wishes.

_____

18. Did you win first prize?

_____

19. The children played in the sun.

_____

20. There are not many days until my birthday.

_____

21. We packed our bags for the trip.

10 ○ read
    ○ two
    ○ storys

11 ○ teacher
    ○ calld
    ○ name

12 ○ give
    ○ hir
    ○ turn

13 ○ carful
    ○ wake
    ○ father

14 ○ frend
    ○ riding
    ○ bike

15 ○ pick
    ○ toyes
    ○ leave

16 ○ fell
    ○ bumped
    ○ noze

17 ○ girl
    ○ three
    ○ wishs

18 ○ win
    ○ first
    ○ prise

19 ○ children
    ○ playd
    ○ sun

20 ○ many
    ○ dayes
    ○ until

21 ○ packt
    ○ bags
    ○ trip

STOP

Letter answers are provided for each question. When the first choice is correct, the answer is A. When the second choice is correct, the answer is B. When the third or fourth choices are correct, the answers are C or D, respectively.

UNIT 1:
WORD STUDY SKILLS
p. 8 1. B 2. A 3. C 4. A 5. A 6. C 7. C 8. A

p. 9 1. B 2. A 3. C 4. A 5. B 6. C 7. B 8. C

p. 10 1. C 2. A 3. B 4. B 5. C 6. A 7. B 8. A

p. 11 1. B 2. C 3. B 4. A 5. C 6. A 7. C 8. B 9. C 10. A

p. 12 1. A 2. C 3. A 4. C 5. C 6. A 7. C 8. C

p. 13 1. B 2. A 3. C 4. C 5. B 6. C 7. B 8. C

UNIT 2:
SIX READING SKILLS
pp. 14–15 1. B 2. A 3. B 4. C 5. C 6. A 7. B 8. A

pp. 16–17 1. C 2. B

p. 18 1. B 2. C 3. B

pp. 19–20 1. B 2. A 3. C 4. B 5. C 6. A

pp. 21–22 1. B 2. A 3. C 4. A

pp. 23–24 1. C 2. B

p. 25 1. B 2. C

UNIT 3: READING COMPREHENSION
p. 26 1. B 2. C 3. B 4. C 5. A

p. 27 1. C 2. C 3. B 4. B 5. A 6. C 7. A 8. B

pp. 28–29 1. A 2. B 3. C 4. B 5. two 6. B 7. A 8. A

pp. 30–33 1. A 2. C 3. B 4. C 5. B 6. B 7. B 8. A 9. C 10. A 11. C 12. A 13. B 14. C 15. C 16. in the yard 17. A 18. C 19. A 20. C 21. 600 22. B 23. A

UNIT 4:
MATH PROBLEM-SOLVING PLAN
p. 35 **Step 1.** Will Tania's fish fit in the new tank? **Step 2.** The tank holds 15 fish. There are 6 goldfish and 5 guppies. **Step 3.** Add to see how many fish Tania has. **Step 4.** 6 + 5 = 11. There are 11 fish. The tank can hold more than 11 fish, so it is large enough. **Step 5.** Yes, because 11 is smaller than 15.

p. 36 **Step 1.** When will he begin to feed the third lion? **Step 2.** He starts feeding at noon. It takes 5 minutes to feed each lion. **Step 3.** You can make a list of feeding times. **Step 4.** First lion: 12:00 to 12:05. Second lion: 12:05 to 12:10. Third lion: 12:10 to 12:15. He begins to feed the third lion at 12:10. **Step 5.** Yes, because the third lion begins eat after 10 minutes.

UNIT 5:
MATH PROBLEM SOLVING
p. 37 1. C 2. A 3. B 4. D 5. 11

p. 38 1. A 2. D 3. D 4. B

p. 39 1. B 2. B 3. C 4. C

p. 40 1. B 2. 5 3. C

p. 41 1. A 2. D 3. C 4. B

p. 42 1. C 2. D 3. D 4. November 18

p. 43 1. B 2. A 3. A

p. 44 1. B 2. A 3. D 4. 8

p. 45 1. C 2. A 3. C 4. 68 5. C 6. C 7. A 8. 40 9. C 10. A

pp. 46–51 1. 2 2. C 3. C 4. C 5. C 6. D 7. B 8. A 9. 50 10. B 11. C 12. 3 13. B 14. A 15. C 16. A 17. B 18. 11 19. B 20. A 21. D 22. C 23. B 24. 69 25. D 26. A 27. C 28. C 29. C 30. 60 31. C

UNIT 6:
LISTENING
p. 53 1. C 2. B 3. B 4. A 5. A 6. B 7. A
8. C 9. A 10. B 11. C 12. C

p. 55 1. C 2. B 3. A 4. C 5. A 6. A
7. B 8. A

p. 57 1. A 2. A 3. B 4. C 5. C 6. A
7. B 8. A

pp. 59–63 1. C 2. C 3. A 4. A 5. B 6. B
7. C 8. A 9. A 10. A 11. B 12. C 13. B
14. C 15. B 16. A 17. A 18. C 19. A
20. A 21. A 22. A 23. C 24. A 25. C
26. C 27. B 28. B 29. A 30. C 31. B
32. A 33. B

UNIT 7:
LANGUAGE
p. 65 1. C 2. C 3. B 4. B 5. A

pp. 67–71 1. B 2. A 3. B 4. C 5. C 6. C
7. B 8. A 9. B 10. C 11. B 12. C

p. 73 1. A 2. C 3. A 4. A 5. C 6. C
7. A 8. B 9. A 10. B 11. C 12. A

pp. 75–81 1. B 2. C 3. B 4. C 5. A 6. A
7. B 8. B 9. C 10. A 11. C 12. B 13. B
14. A 15. C 16. B 17. B 18. C 19. C
20. B 21. A 22. B 23. B 24. A

UNIT 8:
PRACTICE TEST 1:
WORD STUDY SKILLS
pp. 83–89 1. A 2. B 3. C 4. A 5. C 6. B
7. C 8. A 9. C 10. A 11. C 12. B 13. A
14. C 15. C 16. B 17. C 18. A 19. C 20.
A 21. B 22. C 23. B 24. C 25. A 26. B
27. B 28. A 29. C 30. C 31. A 32. B 33.
C 34. A 35. C 36. A 37. A 38. B 39. B
40. C 41. A 42. A 43. C 44. C

UNIT 9: PRACTICE TEST 2:
READING COMPREHENSION
pp. 91–97 1. B 2. A 3. B 4. C 5. C 6. B
7. A 8. B 9. B 10. A 11. B 12. B 13. A
14. C 15. B 16. C 17. C 18. C 19. C
20. B 21. A 22. C 23. two 24. A 25. C

UNIT 10:
PRACTICE TEST 3:
MATH PROBLEM SOLVING
pp. 99–107 1. C 2. B 3. A 4. B 5. D 6.
B 7. C 8. A 9. B 10. 8 11. D 12. D 13.
D 14. D 15. C 16. A 17. D 18. B 19. 8
20. C 21. C 22. A 23. A 24. D 25. C
26. B 27. C 28. B

UNIT 11:
PRACTICE TEST 4:
MATH PROCEDURES
pp. 109–113 1. B 2. 11 3. B 4. C 5. 3
6. B 7. C 8. A 9. D 10. 10 11. B 12. D
13. A 14. B 15. C 16. A 17. C 18. 88
19. B 20. A 21. A 22. 41 23. D 24. C
25. 50 26. B 27. C 28. B

UNIT 12:
PRACTICE TEST 5:
LISTENING
pp. 115–119 1. B 2. A 3. A 4. A 5. B
6. B 7. B 8. A 9. C 10. A 11. C 12. B
13. A 14. C 15. B 16. B 17. C 18. B
19. A 20. B 21. C 22. A 23. B 24. A
25. C 26. C 27. B 28. A 29. C 30. C
31. B 32. A 33. B 34. A 35. C 36. B

UNIT 13:
PRACTICE TEST 6:
LANGUAGE
pp. 121–125 1. A 2. A 3. C 4. A 5. C
6. C 7. B 8. C 9. A 10. C 11. B 12. B
13. A 14. A 15. B 16. C 17. C 18. C
19. B 20. B 21. A